Alphabet

Draw a line joining each capital letter in each box to its p[...]

1.		2.		3.		4.		5.	
C	d	A	x	I	j	B	k	N	n
O	q	E	y	L	i	R	h	U	v
D	c	F	e	J	t	H	p	M	u
Q	g	X	f	S	l	K	b	W	w
G	o	Y	a	T	s	P	r	V	m

Print the missing partner letters.

	A a	___ b	___ c
D ___	___ e	F ___	G ___	___ h
___ i	J ___	___ k	___ l	M ___
___ n	___ o	___ p	Q ___	R ___
___ s	___ T	___ u	___ v	W ___
	___ x	___ Y	Z ___	

Print the missing capital letters of the alphabet.

A	B	___	___	___	___	G
___	___	___	K	___	___	___
___	___	___	S	___	___	___
___	___	___	___	___	___	___

NAME _____

2

Alphabet

Print the missing small letters of the alphabet.

a ___ ___ ___ ___ ___ ___ ___

___ ___ ___ j ___ ___ ___ ___

___ ___ ___ ___ ___ ___ t ___

___ ___ ___ x ___ ___

Print the capital letters of the alphabet that come before and after each letter below.

1. ___ T ___	2. ___ H ___	3. ___ X ___	4. ___ C ___	5. ___ N ___
6. ___ E ___	7. ___ S ___	8. ___ P ___	9. ___ D ___	10. ___ G ___
11. ___ M ___	12. ___ I ___	13. ___ F ___	14. ___ Y ___	15. ___ U ___

Print the small letters of the alphabet that come before and after each letter below.

1. ___ b ___	2. ___ w ___	3. ___ r ___	4. ___ j ___	5. ___ o ___
6. ___ g ___	7. ___ t ___	8. ___ k ___	9. ___ q ___	10. ___ v ___
11. ___ f ___	12. ___ l ___	13. ___ e ___	14. ___ c ___	15. ___ y ___

NAME _____

Beginning Consonant Sounds: D, S, T, Z

Say the name of the picture in each box. Circle the letter that has the beginning sound.

1.	2.	3.	4.	5.
d (s) t z	d s t z	d s t z	d s t z	d s t z

6.	7.	8.	9.	10.
d s t z	d s t z	d s t z	d s t z	d s t z

11.	12.	13.	14.	15.
d s t z	d s t z	d s t z	d s t z	d s t z

Say the name of the picture in each box. Write the letter that has the beginning sound.

1.	2.	3.	4.	5.
t	___	___	___	___

6.	7.	8.	9.	10.
___	___	___	___	___

11.	12.	13.	14.	15.
___	___	___	___	___

NAME _____

Ending Consonant Sounds: D, S, T

Say the name of the picture in each box. Circle the letter that has the ending sound.

1. d (s) t	2. d s t	3. d s t	4. d s t	5. d s t
6. d s t	7. d s t	8. d s t	9. d s t	10. d s t
11. d s t	12. d s t	13. d s t	14. d s t	15. d s t

Say the name of the picture in each box. Write the letter that has the ending sound.

1. __s__	2. ___	3. ___	4. ___	5. ___
6. ___	7. ___	8. ___	9. ___	10. ___
11. ___	12. ___	13. ___	14. ___	15. ___

NAME _____

Beginning Consonant Sounds: B, F, P, V

Say the name of the picture in each box. Circle the letter that has the beginning sound.

1.	2.	3.	4.	5.
b (f) p v	b f p v	b f p v	b f p v	b f p v
6.	7.	8.	9.	10.
b f p v	b f p v	b f p v	b f p v	b f p v
11.	12.	13.	14.	15.
b f p v	b f p v	b f p v	b f p v	b f p v

Say the name of the picture in each box. Write the letter that has the beginning sound.

1.	2.	3.	4.	5.
v	___	___	___	___
6.	7.	8.	9.	10.
___	___	___	___	___
11.	12.	13.	14.	15.
___	___	___	___	___

NAME _____

Ending Consonant Sounds: B, F, P, V

Say the name of the picture in each box. Circle the letter that has the ending sound.

1. b f (p) v	2. b f p v	3. b f p v	4. b f p v	5. b f p v
6. b f p v	7. b f p v	8. b f p v	9. b f p v	10. b f p v
11. b f p v	12. b f p v	13. b f p v	14. b f p v	15. b f p v

Say the name of the picture in each box. Write the letter that has the ending sound.

1. ___f___	2. _____	3. _____	4. _____	5. _____
6. _____	7. _____	8. _____	9. _____	10. _____
11. _____	12. _____	13. _____	14. _____	15. _____

NAME _____

Beginning Consonant Sounds: C, G, H, J

Say the name of the picture in each box. Circle the letter that has the beginning sound.

1. c g (h) j	2. c g h j	3. c g h j	4. c g h j	5. c g h j
6. c g h j	7. c g h j	8. c g h j	9. c g h j	10. c g h j
11. c g h j	12. c g h j	13. c g h j	14. c g h j	15. c g h j

Say the name of the picture in each box. Write the letter that has the beginning sound.

1. g	2. _____	3. _____	4. _____	5. _____
6. _____	7. _____	8. _____	9. _____	10. _____
11. _____	12. _____	13. _____	14. _____	15. _____

NAME _____

Beginning Consonant Sounds: K, M, N, QU

Say the name of the picture in each box. Circle the letter or letters that have the beginning sound.

1.	2.	3.	4.	5.
k m (n) qu	k m n qu	k m n qu	k m n qu	k m n qu
6.	7.	8.	9.	10.
k m n qu	k m n qu	k m n qu	k m n qu	k m n qu
11.	12.	13.	14.	15.
k m n qu	k m n qu	k m n qu	k m n qu	k m n qu

Say the name of the picture in each box. Write the letter or letters that have the beginning sound.

1.	2.	3.	4.	5.
__m__	___	___	___	___
6.	7.	8.	9.	10.
___	___	___	___	___
11.	12.	13.	14.	15.
___	___	___	___	___

NAME _____

Ending Consonant Sounds: G, K, M, N

Say the name of the picture in each box. Circle the letter that has the ending sound.

1. g (k) m n	2. g k m n	3. g k m n	4. g k m n	5. g k m n
6. g k m n	7. g k m n	8. g k m n	9. g k m n	10. g k m n
11. g k m n	12. g k m n	13. g k m n	14. g k m n	15. g k m n

Say the name of the picture in each box. Write the letters that have the beginning and ending sounds in the correct spaces under the picture.

1. h | m	2.	3.	4.	5.
6.	7.	8.	9.	10.
11.	12.	13.	14.	15.

NAME _____

Beginning Consonant Sounds: L, R, W, Y

Say the name of the picture in each box. Circle the letter that has the
beginning sound.

1.	2.	3.	4.	5.
l ⓡ w y	l r w y	l r w y	l r w y	l r w y
6.	7.	8.	9.	10.
l r w y	l r w y	l r w y	l r w y	l r w y
11.	12.	13.	14.	15.
l r w y	l r w y	l r w y	l r w y	l r w y

Say the name of the picture in each box. Write the letter that has the
beginning sound.

1.	2.	3.	4.	5.
__w__	___	___	___	___
6.	7.	8.	9.	10.
___	___	___	___	___
11.	12.	13.	14.	15.
___	___	___	___	___

NAME _____

Ending Consonant Sounds: L, R, X

Say the name of the picture in each box. Circle the letter that has the ending sound.

1. (l) r x
2. l r x
3. l r x
4. l r x
5. l r x
6. l r x
7. l r x
8. l r x
9. l r x
10. l r x
11. l r x
12. l r x
13. l r x
14. l r x
15. l r x

Say the name of the picture in each box. Write the letter that has the ending sound.

1. r
2. ___
3. ___
4. ___
5. ___
6. ___
7. ___
8. ___
9. ___
10. ___
11. ___
12. ___
13. ___
14. ___
15. ___

NAME _____

Review of Consonant Sounds

Say the name of the picture in each box. Write the letters that have the beginning and ending sounds in the correct spaces under the picture.

1.	2.	3.	4.
q u n			

5.	6.	7.	8.

9.	10.	11.	12.

13.	14.	15.	16.

17.	18.	19.	20.

NAME _____

Short Vowel Sound: A

Short Vowel Rule

If a word or syllable has only one vowel, and it comes at the beginning or between two consonants, the vowel usually has a short sound.

Say the name of the picture in each box. If the name has the short sound of <u>a</u>, as in <u>ax</u>, write <u>a</u> on the line.

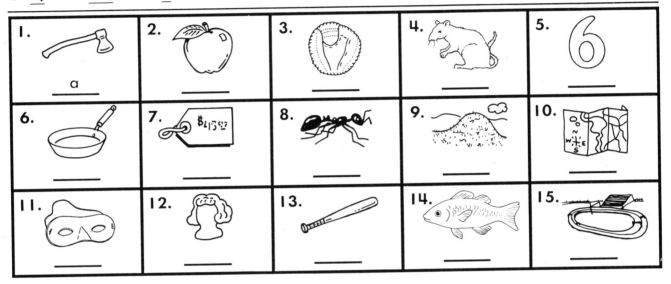

1. a	2.	3.	4.	5.
6.	7.	8.	9.	10.
11.	12.	13.	14.	15.

Say the name of the picture in each box. Circle the name.

1. (tag) tap tack	2. cam can cap	3. man ramp map	4. gab bag lag
5. wax tax ax	6. cap cab sap	7. had bat hat	8. sacks facts tacks
9. damp lamp lamb	10. lamb hand band	11. rat cat rap	12. can fat fan

NAME _____

Short Vowel Sound: A

Say the name of the picture in each box. Write the letter that has the vowel sound.

1. a	2.	3.	4.	5.
___	___	___	___	___
6.	7.	8.	9.	10.
___	___	___	___	___
11.	12.	13.	14.	15.
___	___	___	___	___

Find the word in each box to complete the sentence. Circle the word. Then write it on the line.

1. Jack sat in the cab, and his cat sat on his ___lap___.	pat tap (lap)
2. Sand bags can act as a _____.	dam damp tam
3. Sam has a _____ on his back and an ax in his hand.	tack pack past
4. Jan has a pan and a can of _____ in the pack.	dam ham tam
5. The man on the raft had a map in his _____.	band land hand
6. The _____ ran to the van.	fan tan man

NAME _____

Short Vowel Sound: A

Say the name of the picture in each box. Write the name on the line below.

1. bag	2.	3.	4.
5.	6.	7.	8.
9.	10.	11.	12.

Read the words that are part of each sentence. Finish the sentence by writing the words from box in the correct order.

1. Ann and a ___pal sang at camp___.	camp sang pal at
2. Hank can be the ___.	man at last bat
3. Pam and Jack ran as ___.	as cat the fast
4. The man in the van had a ___.	in hand map his
5. Dad asks Ann and Dan ___.	the tasks do to

NAME ___

Short Vowel Sound: I

Short Vowel Rule

If a word or syllable has only one vowel, and it comes at the beginning or between two consonants, the vowel usually has a short sound.

Say the name of the picture in each box. If the name has the short sound of i, as in six, write i on the line.

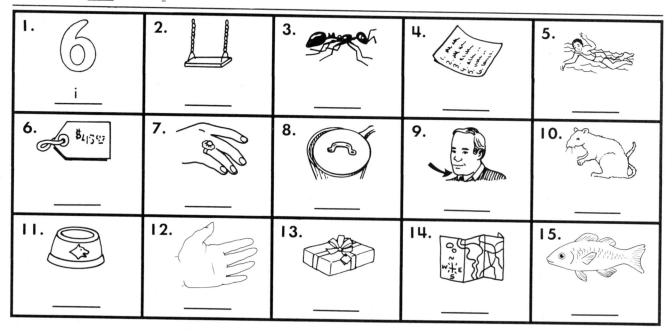

1.	2.	3.	4.	5.
i	___	___	___	___
6.	7.	8.	9.	10.
___	___	___	___	___
11.	12.	13.	14.	15.
___	___	___	___	___

Say the name of the picture in each box. Circle the name.

1.	2.	3.	4.
sick (six) sat	pin pan bin	bill calf hill	mat mitt mill
5.	6.	7.	8.
sank rink sink	ring rang ham	ping pat pig	lips laps dips
9.	10.	11.	12.
list last first	wig wag sag	lift gift past	lid lad list

NAME _____

Short Vowel Sound: I

Say the name of the picture in each box. Write the letter that has the vowel sound.

1. ⬚ ___	2. ⬚ ___	3. ⬚ ___	4. ⬚ ___	5. ⬚ ___
6. ⬚ ___	7. ⬚ ___	8. ⬚ ___	9. ⬚ ___	10. ⬚ ___
11. ⬚ ___	12. ⬚ ___	13. ⬚ ___	14. ⬚ ___	15. ⬚ ___

Find the word in each box to complete the sentence. Circle the word. Then write it on the line.

1. Ask Dan to fill the can with _____milk_____.	mill (milk) bank
2. If Tim can fix the bat, he will _____ a mitt.	ran win pin
3. Nan _____ hang up the pants on the rack.	will mask milk
4. A big _____ hit Sam as he ran.	rank wink wind
5. The pins are in the _____ can.	tan tin tint
6. Jill did not see the cab in the _____.	mast mist miss

NAME _____

Short Vowel Sound: I

Say the name of the picture in each box. Write the name on the line below.

1.	2.	3.	4.
bat	_____	_____	_____
5.	6.	7.	8.
_____	_____	_____	_____
9.	10.	11.	12.
_____	_____	_____	_____

Read the words that are part of each sentence. Finish the sentence by writing the words from the box in the correct order.

1. Tim will fill _his bag with sand_____.	his sand with bag
2. Sid and Kit can _____.	pit a big dig
3. Jim kicks his mitt _____.	is he if mad
4. Nan hits as quick as a _____.	bat with wink the
5. Nick went with Jill to _____.	in sing band a

NAME _____

Short Vowel Sound: U

Short Vowel Rule

If a word or syllable has only one vowel, and it comes at the beginning or between two consonants, the vowel usually has a short sound.

Say the name of the picture in each box. If the name has the short sound of u, as in duck, write u on the line.

1. _u_	2. ___	3. ___	4. ___	5. ___
6. ___	7. ___	8. ___	9. ___	10. ___
11. ___	12. ___	13. ___	14. ___	15. ___

Say the name of the picture in each box. Circle the name.

1. sum nip (sun)	2. gum gun gang	3. tab tub but	4. pin pan nap
5. sip cap cup	6. pun map pin	7. bus but bit	8. cub back duck
9. gab cub cab	10. bugs bags hugs	11. stun bins nuts	12. cast cuff cuts

NAME _____

Short Vowel Sound: U

Say the name of the picture in each box. Write the letter that has the vowel sound.

1.	2.	3.	4.	5.
___	___	___	___	___
6.	7.	8.	9.	10.
___	___	___	___	___
11.	12.	13.	14.	15.
___	___	___	___	___

Find the word in each box to complete the sentence. Circle the word. Then write it on the line.

1. Sis and Dad will hunt for the _____bugs_____.	backs buzz (bugs)
2. Will the pup jump into the _____ full of suds?	but tub tab
3. Jill and Jim _____ run fast, or they will miss the bus.	mist mast must
4. The pup is a _____.	mitt mutt mat
5. It is fun for Pal to _____ at the rug, but he will rip it.	tug tag bug
6. It will be fun to _____ bugs with you, but I must be back at six.	tank hint hunt

NAME _____

Short Vowel Sound: U

Say the name of the picture in each box. Write the name on the line below.

1. cub	2. _____	3. _____	4. _____
5. _____	6. _____	7. _____	8. _____
9. _____	10. _____	11. _____	12. _____

Read the words that are part of each sentence. Finish the sentence by writing the words from the box in the correct order.

1. Is Kim _____ ill with the mumps _____ ?	with mumps ill the
2. The big tank _____ .	rust is of full
3. Dan must jump up to _____ .	up the cup pick
4. A pack of gum was at the _____ .	bus the back of
5. The bus dug a _____ .	the in rut mud

NAME _____

Short Vowel Sound: O

Short Vowel Rule

If a word or syllable has only one vowel, and it comes at the beginning or between two consonants, the vowel usually has a short sound.

Say the name of the picture in each box. If the name has the short sound of <u>o</u>, as in <u>fox</u>, write <u>o</u> on the line.

1.	2.	3.	4.	5.
____o____	_____	_____	_____	_____
6.	7.	8.	9.	10.
_____	_____	_____	_____	_____
11.	12.	13.	14.	15.
_____	_____	_____	_____	_____

Say the name of the picture in each box. Circle the name.

1.	2.	3.	4.
tap pat (top)	fix fox box	sock sack sick	bill full hill
5.	6.	7.	8.
rod rid rug	cat cot cut	can pot cat	lack lock luck
9.	10.	11.	12.
pat top pot	box fox back	sock rack rock	dull dill doll

NAME _____

Short Vowel Sound: O

Say the name of the picture in each box. Write the letter that has the vowel sound.

1. o	2. ___	3. ___	4. ___	5. ___
6. ___	7. ___	8. ___	9. ___	10. ___
11. ___	12. ___	13. ___	14. ___	15. ___

Find the word in each box to complete the sentence. Circle the word. Then write it on the line.

1. The fox hid in the rocks on _____top_____ of the hill.	tip (top) tap
2. Did Mom ask Don to pick up his _____?	luck docks socks
3. Dot can _____ the ring at the pin and hit it.	lass toss loss
4. Jan had a lock for the box, but it is _____.	last list lost
5. The dog picks the _____, the fox picks the cat, and the cat picks the rat.	fit fix fox
6. Tom will fix the dock on the big _____ for his raft.	band pond quit

NAME _____

Short Vowel Sound: O

Say the name of the picture in each box. Write the name on the line below.

1. box	2.	3.	4.
5.	6.	7.	8.
9.	10.	11.	12.

Read the words that are part of each sentence. Finish the sentence by writing the words from the box in the correct order.

1. Mom has _a job for Bob_____.	for a job Bob
2. Dot cannot _____.	the lift hot pot
3. Jill got rid of _____.	junk of the box
4. The dog cannot _____.	jump the cot on
5. It is not odd to see a lot of _____.	rocks hill the on

NAME _____

Short Vowel Sound: E

25

Short Vowel Rule

If a word or syllable has one one vowel, and it comes at the beginning or between two consonants, the vowel usually has a short sound.

Say the name of the picture in each box. If the name has the short sound of e, as in jet, write e on the line.

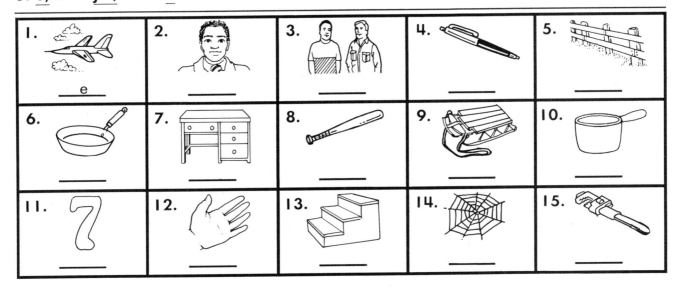

Say the name of the picture in each box. Circle the name.

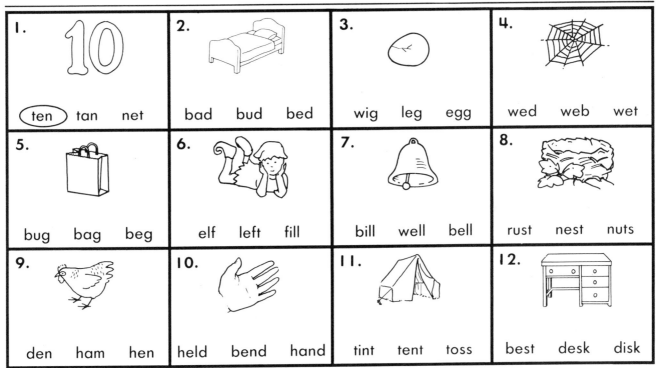

1. (ten)   tan   net
2. bad   bud   bed
3. wig   leg   egg
4. wed   web   wet
5. bug   bag   beg
6. elf   left   fill
7. bill   well   bell
8. rust   nest   nuts
9. den   ham   hen
10. held   bend   hand
11. tint   tent   toss
12. best   desk   disk

NAME _____

Short Vowel Sound: E

Say the name of the picture in each box. Write the letter that has the vowel sound.

1. _e_	2. ___	3. ___	4. ___	5. ___
6. ___	7. ___	8. ___	9. ___	10. ___
11. ___	12. ___	13. ___	14. ___	15. ___

Find the word in each box to complete the sentence. Circle the word. Then write it on the line.

1. The hen sits on ten eggs in the _____nest_____.	(nest) nuts mast
2. Just as Ed and Pam met, the sun sank in the _____.	nest well west
3. Ned fell off the bed and got a bump on his _____ hand.	left felt loft
4. The _____ had tan pants, little red vests, and red felt hats.	elms selves elves
5. If Jen sets up the tent, Jeff will _____.	kept help held
6. If you will dust the desk for me, I will _____ you my best pen.	land lend lent

NAME _____

Short Vowel Sound: E

27

Say the name of the picture in each box. Write the name on the line below.

1. ten	2.	3.	4.
5.	6.	7.	8.
9.	10.	11.	12.

Read the words that are part of each sentence. Finish the sentence by writing the words from the box in the correct order.

1. The big elk _____ sped by the men _____.	by men the sped
2. Ted's well-fed pet is _____.	red big a hen
3. Jeff has the mumps, but he _____.	fast get well will
4. Tell Bess to mend the big rip _____.	Meg's in tent red
5. Meg went on a trip _____.	a jet big in

NAME _____

Short Vowel Compound Words

A **compound word** is made up of two or more one-syllable words. Circle each one-syllable word in the compound words below.

1. (sand)(box)	2. bedbug	3. muskrat	4. dustpan	5. uphill	6. airplane
7. cobweb	8. pickax	9. hatpin	10. itself	11. handbag	12. football
13. himself	14. cannot	15. hilltop	16. sunset	17. padlock	18. bellhop
19. cockpit	20. pigpen	21. upset	22. bulldog	23. handcuffs	24. windmill

Find the compound word in each box to complete the sentence. Circle the word. Then write the word on the line.

1. Jan and Ken ran ____uphill____ to the sandbox.	replace (uphill) hilltop
2. The bulldog was _____ by the muskrat.	uphill sunset upset
3. Tess will look into the _____ of the jet.	cockpit cobweb cannot
4. Edwin cannot unlock the _____.	pigpen pickax padlock
5. The handbag held a set of _____.	windmills himself handcuffs
6. We dusted the _____ from the ceiling.	cockpit cobwebs dustpans

NAME _____

Long Vowels: A, I

The word cape has the long sound of the vowel a. Say the name of the picture in each box. If the name has the long sound of a, circle the picture.

1.	2.	3.	4.	5.
6.	7.	8.	9.	10.
11.	12.	13.	14.	15.
16.	17.	18.	19.	20.
21.	22.	23.	24.	25.

The word pie has the long sound of the vowel i. Say the name of the picture in each box. If the name has the long sound of i, circle the picture.

1.	2.	3.	4.	5.
6.	7.	8.	9.	10.
11.	12.	13.	14.	15.
16.	17.	18.	19.	20.
21.	22.	23.	24.	25.

NAME _____

Long Vowel Sounds: A, I

Long Vowel Rule I

If a syllable or a one-syllable word has two vowels, the first vowel usually has a long sound and the second vowel is silent.

The short vowel words in the first column of each box have been changed to long vowel words in the second column. Draw a line to join these words.

1.	am	aim	**2.**	bit	died
	pal	paint		did	wine
	can	pail		win	dime
	pant	cane		dim	bite
3.	cam	came	**4.**	rip	hide
	at	made		quit	ripe
	mad	ate		hid	pine
	van	vane		pin	quite
5.	past	rain	**6.**	kit	time
	man	main		rid	kite
	fat	paste		fin	fine
	ran	fate		Tim	ride

Find the word in each box to complete the sentence. Circle the word. Write the word on the line.

1. Her name is Mame, and my name is the ____same____.	nine (same) name
2. If you bake a cake, may I have a _____?	past haste taste
3. Kit will _____ the ball at the pine tree.	am dime aim
4. Dave just ate, so he must _____ to dive into the lake.	wide wait wick
5. The limeade was made with five limes, and it tastes just _____.	fine take fin
6. The last time we went to camp, you lost a pail in the _____.	bake lad lake

NAME _____

Long Vowel Sounds: A, I

Say the name of the picture in each box. Then write the missing long vowel.

1.	2.	3.	4.
c _a_ ne	c ___ pe	b ___ ke	g ___ te
5.	6.	7.	8.
k ___ te	p ___ il	r ___ de	p ___ e
9.	10.	11.	12.
l ___ ke	t ___ re	d ___ ve	r ___ in

Read the words that are part of each sentence. Finish the sentence by writing the words from the box in the correct order.

1. Elaine's dog likes to __race to the gate__.	to race gate the
2. Jane gave Jack a _____.	bike on the ride
3. The lions are tame _____.	not and will bite
4. Will it take a long time to _____?	to the lake ride
5. Tom, wake up Dave, and tell him _____.	his make bed to

NAME _____

Long Vowel Sounds: U, O

The word <u>cube</u> has the long sound of the vowel u. Say the name of the
picture in each box. If the name has the long sound of u, circle the picture.

1.	2.	3.	4.	5.
6.	7.	8.	9.	10.
11.	12.	13.	14.	15.
16.	17.	18.	19.	20.
21.	22.	23.	24.	25.

The word <u>toad</u> has the long sound of the vowel o. Say the name of the
picture in each box. If the name has the long sound of o, circle the picture.

1.	2.	3.	4.	5.
6.	7.	8.	9.	10.
11.	12.	13.	14.	15.
16.	17.	18.	19.	20.
21.	22.	23.	24.	25.

NAME _____

Long Vowel Sounds: U, O

Long Vowel Rule

If a syllable or a one-syllable word has two vowels, the first vowel usually has a long sound and the second vowel is silent.

The short vowel words in the first column of each box have been changed to long vowel words in the second column. Draw a line to join these words.

1.			2.		
	tub	cape		mop	node
	Al	tube		not	road
	cap	cute		rod	mope
	cut	use		cot	note
	us	ail		nod	coat
3.	Sid	robe	**4.**	sop	tote
	rob	hope		got	soap
	cub	rate		Tod	code
	rat	side		tot	goat
	hop	cube		cod	toad

Find the word in each box to complete the sentence. Circle the word. Then write it on the line.

1. Hank wore yellow socks with a red _____coat_____ and tie.	coal toad (coat)
2. The tile can _____ a coat of wax to make it shine.	use sue cue
3. Tom will ride his bike past the load of hay on the _____.	rod road rode
4. When the loan is _____ Luke will repay it.	doe due hue
5. Sue rode to the picnic on the bare back of a _____.	mile suit mule
6. June's dog awoke to see Spot run away with his _____.	made bone dome

NAME _____

Long Vowel Sounds: U, O

Say the name of the picture in each box. Then write the missing long vowel.

1. b __o__ ne	2. t ____ be	3. m ____ le	4. n ____ se
5. r ____ pe	6. f ____ se	7. d ____ me	8. t ____ ne
9. c ____ be	10. g ____ at	11. r ____ le	12. t ____ ad

Read the words that are part of each sentence. Finish the sentence by writing the words from the box in the correct order.

1. June laid the red _____ tube on the desk _____.	desk the on tube
2. If Luke lies on his _____.	he doze bed will
3. The baby rode home on the back _____.	tame of goat a
4. Joe and Sue _____.	will tune a play
5. No, Tom, you may _____.	row boat the not

NAME _____

Long Vowel Sound: E

Long Vowel Rule I

If a syllable or a one-syllable word has two vowels, the first vowel usually has a long sound and the second vowel is silent.

The word **seal** has the long sound of the vowel **e**. Say the name of the picture in each box. If the name has the long sound of **e**, circle the picture.

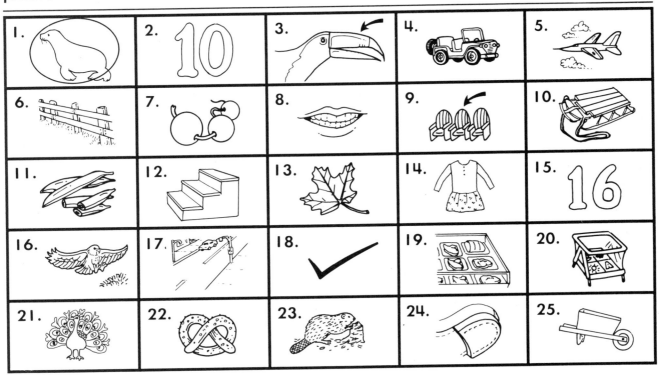

The short vowel words in the first column of each box have been changed to long vowel words in the second column. Draw a line to join these words.

1.			2.		
	red	need		set	cute
	Ben	peep		bed	kite
	pep	bean		cut	Pete
	bet	read		pet	seat
	Ned	beat		kit	bead
3.			4.		
	pad	feed		led	mean
	met	hide		net	weed
	ten	meet		wed	lead
	fed	paid		men	beast
	hid	teen		best	neat

NAME _____

Long Vowel Sound: E

Say the name of the picture in each box. Then write the missing vowel.

1. j _e_ ep	2. f ___ et	3. p ___ pe	4. b ___ e
5. t ___ ad	6. qu ___ en	7. l ___ af	8. c ___ be
9. s ___ at	10. r ___ ke	11. s ___ al	12. b ___ ads

Read the words that are part of each sentence. Finish the sentence by writing the words from the box in the correct order.

1. The more we read, the more ___we like to read___.	like / read / to / we
2. The size of the desk top is four _____.	feet / feet / five / by
3. The deer got too near the _____.	in / tree / bees / the
4. The least we can do is to make Pete _____.	at / here / feel / home
5. Jean will feed the geese, and Red _____.	feed / will / seals / the

NAME _____

Long Vowel Compound Words

A compound word is made up of two or more one-syllable words. Circle each one-syllable word in the compound words below.

1. (rail)(road)	2. raincoat	3. beehive	4. sailboat	5. maybe	6. lifetime
7. beside	8. teammate	9. homemade	10. oatmeal	11. mealtime	12. seahorse
13. pipeline	14. cupcake	15. lifeboat	16. seacoast	17. hayride	18. fireside
19. necktie	20. subway	21. fireboat	22. rainbow	23. forecast	24. rowboat

Find the compound word in each box to complete the sentence. Circle the word. Then write the word on the line.

1. If you do not have a ___raincoat___, you will get wet.	(raincoat) rainbow mudhole
2. Maybe we can go on a _____ at the fair.	homemade hayride fireside
3. Tom and his dad ride the _____ each day.	away subway sunset
4. The cab will stop beside the _____.	rainbow lifetime railroad
5. Lots of red and yellow sails can be seen along the _____.	sandman seacoast mailbox
6. As the sun came out after the rain, we saw a _____ in the east.	necktie railway rainbow

NAME _____

R Blends

Say the name of the picture in each box. Circle the letters that form the beginning blend.

1. br (cr) dr	2. br cr dr	3. br cr dr	4. br cr dr	5. br cr dr
6. dr fr gr	7. dr fr gr	8. dr fr gr	9. dr fr gr	10. dr fr gr
11. gr pr tr	12. gr pr tr	13. gr pr tr	14. gr pr tr	15. gr pr tr

Find the word in each box to complete the sentence. Circle the word. Then write it on the line.

1. The name of Fred's green pet _____frog_____ is Hank.	dog (frog) from
2. Brenda will open the old _____ in the attic.	trick track trunk
3. Will Dad treat us to a _____ of lemonade?	drank drink trunk
4. If Ted wins the drum contest, his _____ will be a bike.	prize tries dries
5. The train tracks ran along the creek but did not _____ it.	grass crow cross
6. Fran and Frank crept along until they came to the soft green _____ .	cross grass press

NAME _____

R Blends

Say the name of the picture in each box. Then write the missing letters to form the beginning blend.

1. ___ c ___ r ab	2. _____ um	3. _____ og	4. _____ ee
5. _____ ack	6. ___ ___ ize	7. _____ ess	8. _____ ame
9. _____ ayon	10. _____ ide	11. _____ uit	12. _____ apes

Read the words that are part of each sentence. Finish the sentence by writing the words from the box in the correct order.

1. If you do not tie the boat, _____it will drift away_____ .	away it drift will
2. To stop a car, you _____ .	the use brakes must
3. Dates, nuts, and fruit _____ .	a treat are real
4. The horse likes to _____ .	the grass graze in
5. Bret's home is _____ .	made bricks red of

NAME _____

L Blends

Say the name of the picture in each box. Circle the letters that form the beginning blend.

1. (bl) cl fl	2. bl cl fl	3. bl cl fl	4. bl cl fl	5. bl cl fl
6. cl fl gl	7. cl fl gl	8. cl fl gl	9. cl fl gl	10. cl fl gl
11. fl gl pl	12. fl gl pl	13. fl gl pl	14. fl gl pl	15. fl gl pl

Find the word in each box to complete the sentence. Circle the word. Then write it on the line.

1. Nine _____plus_____ ten is nineteen. — (plus) plan club

2. As the wind _____, it fills the sails of the boat. — blame blows crows

3. Eat the salad on your plate and drink the _____ of milk. — class clap glass

4. The _____ of the fire are red, yellow, and blue. — blames flames flags

5. Claire can fix the _____ with glue. — gloat clock black

6. Please do not plant the _____ too near the driveway. — float treat tree

NAME _____

L Blends

Say the name of the picture in each box. Then write the missing letters to form the beginning blend.

1. __c_ __l__ own	2. _____ _____ ag	3. _____ _____ ade	4. _____ _____ ock
5. _____ _____ oat	6. _____ _____ ug	7. _____ _____ obe	8. _____ _____ ap
9. _____ _____ ass	10. _____ _____ ock	11. _____ _____ ant	12. _____ _____ ue

Read the words that are part of each sentence. Finish the sentence by writing the words from the box in the correct order.

1. Blast-off time for the _____ rocket is nine o'clock _____.	o'clock nine is rocket
2. Clem wore a long blond _____.	in the wig play
3. If we sleep in the tent, we will _____.	lots need blankets of
4. Claire and Glen will _____.	raft on float a
5. The flag on the train will _____.	the flap wind in

NAME _____

S Blends

42

Say the name of the picture in each box. Circle the letters that form the beginning blend.

1. (sk) sl sm	2. sk sl sm	3. sk sl sm	4. sk sl sm	5. sk sl sm
6. sn sp sw	7. sn sp sw	8. sn sp sw	9. sn sp sw	10. sn sp sw
11. scr spl str	12. scr spl str	13. scr spl str	14. scr spr str	15. scr spr str

Find the word in each box to complete the sentence. Circle the word. Then write it on the line.

1. It takes ____skill____ to swim or dive well. | skull (skill) scale

2. A lot of steep _____ lead down to the subway. | stairs stoves snakes

3. The green and blue _____ belongs to Glen. | stub slid sled

4. You may play on the _____, but do not play on the slide. | smoke swim swing

5. Jim slipped and fell off his bike in the _____. | street stun streak

6. If you _____ milk on the hot stove, it will smoke. | snake spill smell

NAME _____

S Blends

Say the name of the picture in each box. Then write the missing letters to form the beginning blend.

1. __s__ __k__ ate	2. _____ ed	3. _____ are	4. _____ oke
5. _____ ake	6. _____ im	7. _____ it	8. _____ ove
9. _____ ill	10. _____ eet	11. _____ ub	12. _____ ing

Read the words that are part of each sentence. Finish the sentence by writing the words from the box in the correct order.

1. Please tell me the _plot of the story___.	of story plot the
2. Tim and his classmates plan to _____.	steel a visit mill
3. Blaire will use the _____.	driveway skateboard the on
4. I saw _____ at the fire.	stream smoke a of
5. The rains help the buds on the trees _____.	swell to and open

NAME _____

Consonant Digraphs: TH, WH

The word <u>think</u> begins with a sound of th. Say the name of the picture in each box. If the name begins with a sound of th, circle the picture.

1.	2.	3.	4.	5.
6.	7.	8.	9.	10.
11.	12.	13.	14.	15.

The word <u>wheel</u> begins with the sound of wh. Say the name of the picture in each box. If the name begins with the sound of wh, write wh on the line.

1. wh	2. ___	3. ___	4. ___	5. ___
6. ___	7. ___	8. ___	9. ___	10. ___
11. ___	12. ___	13. ___	14. ___	15. ___

NAME _____

Consonant Digraphs: SH, CH

The word **ship** begins with the sound of <u>sh</u>. Say the name of the picture in each box. If the name begins with the sound of <u>sh</u>, circle the picture.

1.	2.	3.	4.	5.
6.	7.	8.	9.	10.
11.	12.	13.	14.	15.

The word **checkers** begins with the sound of <u>ch</u>. Say the name of the picture in each box. If the name begins with the sound of <u>ch</u>, write <u>ch</u> on the line.

1.	2.	3.	4.	5.
ch	___	___	___	___
6.	7.	8.	9.	10.
___	___	___	___	___
11.	12.	13.	14.	15.
___	___	___	___	___

NAME _____

46

Consonant Digraphs

Say the name of the picture in each box. Circle the letters that form the beginning or ending digraph.

1.	2.	3.	4.
th (wh) sh ch	th wh sh ch	th wh sh ch	th wh sh ch

5.	6.	7.	8.
th wh sh ch	th wh sh ch	th wh sh ch	th wh sh ch

9.	10.	11.	12.
th wh sh ch	th wh sh ch	th wh sh ch	th wh sh ch

13.	14.	15.	16.
th wh sh ch	th wh sh ch	th wh sh ch	th wh sh ch

17.	18.	19.	20.
th wh sh ch	th wh sh ch	th wh sh ch	th wh sh ch

21.	22.	23.	24.
th wh sh ch	th wh sh ch	th wh sh ch	th wh sh ch

NAME _____

Consonant Digraphs

Say the name of the picture in each box. Circle the name.

1.	2.	3.	4.
sharp (sheep)	these tree	chicks checks	width wheat
sleep steep	three theme	shakes cheeks	whale white

5.	6.	7.	8.
whale ahead	chin chain	shift thick	third dirty
while wheel	shin clan	ship trap	thirty thin

9.	10.	11.	12.
chair chain	wept whip	spears cheery	moth mitt
shame claim	wipe what	smear cherry	math melt

13.	14.	15.	16.
fist lash	tones thrown	much mush	thimble whittle
fish last	these throne	crutch catch	whistle thistle

17.	18.	19.	20.
thrush teach	sheer cheer	fishbone wishbone	when cheat
teeth thrust	sheen chair	whichever whenever	wheat three

21.	22.	23.	24.
child chimney	wheelbarrow wheel	chimp shipment	chatter shatter
chill children	welcome which	champion chipmunk	shining shadow

NAME _____

Consonant Digraphs

Read the words that are part of each sentence. Finish the sentence by writing the words from the box in the correct order.

1. Which child wishes to _help with the dishes_ ?	help the with dishes
2. The sheep that graze _____.	coats here thick have
3. Carlos has seen a _____.	the near whale beach
4. Tom rests his chin on his _____.	thinks he when hand
5. May will catch _____.	Chip pitch will and
6. Who will whip the cream for the top _____?	the of cake chocolate
7. When you leave the cabin, please _____.	door kitchen shut the
8. The chimpanzee ate a banana from _____.	the fruit of dish
9. After lunch, we used the wishbone _____.	and wish made a
10. Three thin coats of wax will _____.	shine floor a make
11. We can hear the chatter of a _____.	the in forest chipmunk

NAME _____

Y and W as Vowels

When y and w come at the beginning of a word or syllable, they are consonants.
When y and w come at the end of a word or syllable, they are vowels.

Read each sentence. Underline each y or w that is a consonant. Circle each y or w that is a vowel.

1. Silly Willy will play in the wet clay.

2. Wipe your muddy feet on the mat by the door.

3. Tammy, may we wade in the shallow creek?

4. On the way home we met a stray dog.

5. The snowman that we made last year wore a bow tie.

6. The black crow will try to steal the candy from the sly fox.

7. In the story, the white eagle flies up into the sky.

8. Kay will open the yellow drapes and close the window.

9. Tom will plant trees today in the backyard, and his wife will sow grass seed.

10. Can you stay with my baby? He will wake up at ten o'clock and cry for milk.

11. A strong wind can blow the dry sand miles beyond the windmill.

Make a list of all the words from the sentences above in which y and w are silent vowels.

Silent Y Words		Silent W Words	
play			

NAME _____

Y as a Vowel

1. When y is the only vowel at the end of a one-syllable word, it has the long sound of the vowel i.
2. When y comes at the end of a word that has more than one syllable, it usually has the long sound of the vowel e.

Read each word. Write it in the correct column.

by	sly	happy	windy	dry	try
taffy	Molly	silly	fly	lucky	cry

Y has the long sound of i.		Y has the long sound of e.	
by	_____	_____	_____
_____	_____	_____	_____
_____	_____	_____	_____

Read the words that are part of each sentence. Finish the sentence by writing the words from the box in the correct order.

1. Hoppy, the bunny, likes to play ___with the shy chipmunk___.	the shy with chipmunk
2. Today Sandy and I will _____.	to capital the fly
3. Why is the grass so green and _____?	so sky blue the
4. Molly is happy to _____.	a have puppy tiny

NAME _____

Hard and Soft Sounds of C

When c is followed by e, i, or y, it usually has a soft sound, or the sound of s.

Say the name of the picture in each box. If the name has the soft sound of c, write c on the line.

1. c	2.	3.	4.	5.
6.	7.	8.	9.	10.
11.	12	13.	14.	15.

Say the name of the picture in each box. Circle the name.

1. press price (prince) brick	2. same core came care	3. face fact lace fake	4. nice Mike mice rice	5. cry crow down crown
6. cane care cans case	7. cinema cite citizen city	8. crab crow base wore	9. side dice cite doze	10. prince pants pencil punts
11. fence chance fancy cinch	12. since priceless prince princess	13. necktie central necklace cement	14. comet camel sell cell	15. camels canals cygnet cymbals

NAME _____

Hard and Soft Sounds of G

When g is followed by e, i, or y, it usually has a soft sound, or the sound of j.

Say the name of the picture in each box. If the name has the soft sound of g, write g on the line.

1. ___g___	2. _____	3. _____	4. _____	5. _____
6. _____	7. _____	8. _____	9. _____	10. _____
11. _____	12. _____	13. _____	14. _____	15. _____

Say the name of the picture in each box. Circle the name.

1. gum (gem) gym mug	2. goal gate goat page	3. gain gum pain game	4. cage Gene wage gave	5. pledge flag plug pony
6. gale huge gate page	7. gem gym mug gum	8. grand grant groan giant	9. state shape stage paste	10. frog fond flag flap
11. pledge badge bridge change	12. grades dragon giblets drapes	13. gelatin garden giblets genius	14. globe giraffe glide job	15. gruff giant giraffe graft

NAME _____

Soft Sounds of C and G

Say the name of the picture in each box. Write the name on the line below.

1. _____cage_____	2. _____	3. _____	4. _____
5. _____	6. _____	7. _____	8. _____
9. _____	10. _____	11. _____	12. _____

Find the word in each box to complete the sentence. Circle the word. Then write it on the line.

1. The ____prince____ and princess live with the queen.	price (prince) prints
2. The _____ on the pond is too thin to skate on.	ice ace act
3. We had to cross a huge _____ to go over the river.	badge brick bridge
4. We must clean the cabin to get rid of the _____ and cockroaches.	nice mice race
5. When Gene paid, he received twenty cents in_____.	chicks chance change

NAME _____

Soft Sounds of C and G

Read the words that are part of each sentence. Finish the sentence by writing the words from the box in the correct order.

1. Cindy and Grace keep the ___canary in a cage___.	a in canary cage
2. Janice and Bill like to dance _____.	music to nice the
3. A puppy must think that a _____.	is giant a giraffe
4. The police will help you cross the _____.	in city street the
5. Nancy cannot decide whether to _____.	circus the go to
6. The children like to play dodge ball _____.	on city the beach
7. At the Olympic Games, we sat _____.	the judges' near stand
8. Tracey wore make-up on her _____.	face play the for
9. Coach Lodge will be _____.	new gym the teacher
10. While Gene read the story, the class _____.	in circle sat a
11. The gems are on display at the _____.	palace the to entrance

NAME _____

AR

The word <u>arm</u> has the sound of ar. Say the name of the picture in each box. If the name has the sound of ar, write ar on the line.

1.	2.	3.	4.	5.
__ar__	_____	_____	_____	_____
6.	7.	8.	9.	10.
_____	_____	_____	_____	_____
11.	12.	13.	14.	15.
_____	_____	_____	_____	_____

Say the name of the picture in each box. Circle the name.

1.	2.	3.	4.	5.
care (car) cane can	are air arm ore	yard jars yarn bark	cart cares card yard	carve card crave cart
6.	7.	8.	9.	10.
tar jam far jar	yard yarn rake rain	dark darn dart dirt	star stay stare stir	bend burn band barn
11.	12.	13.	14.	15.
fact taps tart stop	hard harp dark sharp	inch chin arch shin	sparks spends spanks spins	grass garment graze garden

NAME _____

OR

The word <u>corn</u> has the sound of <u>or</u>. Say the name of the picture in each box. If the name has the sound of <u>or</u>, write <u>or</u> on the line.

1. __or__	2. ____	3. ____	4. ____	5. ____
6. ____	7. ____	8. ____	9. ____	10. ____
11. ____	12. ____	13. ____	14. ____	15. ____

Say the name of the picture in each box. Circle the name.

1.	2.	3.	4.	5.
core ran care (car)	corn cart core rain	cork corn card core	ford fast fort from	fifty fairy forty fancy
6.	7.	8.	9.	10.
hard horn dart born	fact fork tank ford	dense hard horse barn	barn base born bare	shine thorn shave throne
11.	12.	13.	14.	15.
skunk storm stork steam	store star stone stare	store star stone stare	pinch perch porch chore	teach chart torch short

NAME _____

AR, OR

Say the name of the picture in each box. Then write the missing letters.

1. c __a__ __ __ r	2. __ __ __ m	3. f __ __ t	4. y __ __ n
5. c __ __ __ n	6. f __ __ k	7. j __ __ __	8. b __ __ n
9. d __ __ t	10. st __ __ k	11. h __ __ n	12. st __ __ __
13. t __ __ ch	14. y __ __ d	15. th __ __ n	16. h __ __ p
17. f __ __ ty	18. sp __ __ ks	19. t __ __ t	20. h __ __ se
21. p __ __ ch	22. p __ __ cupine	23. c __ __ t	24. g __ __ den

NAME _____

AR, OR

Find the word in each box to complete the sentence. Circle the word. Then write it on the line.

1. Norman tied the parcel with a strong _____cord_____.	card ⟨cord⟩ cork
2. The target for the space probe is _____.	Marty Mrs. Mars
3. We can pack sandwiches for the picnic in this _____.	carpet carton arctic
4. Please send these _____ to the City Dress Shop.	gardens garments parsnips
5. The _____ reared up and upset the fruit cart.	horns harsh horse

Read the words that are part of each sentence. Finish the sentence by writing the words from the box in the correct order.

1. It is a nice morning to _____start on a trip_____.	trip on a start
2. Marty can use his _____.	class swimming snorkel in
3. Marta stored the _____.	the porch on corn
4. The ship came into port with _____.	a cars of load
5. We will bring parsley from the _____.	the for market salad

NAME _____

IR, UR, ER

The word bird has the sound of ir. The letters ir, ur, and er have the same sound. Say the name of the picture in each box. Circle the name.

1.	2.	3.	4.
(bird) bride Burt burst	shirt short skirt start	thirsty thirty thirteen thrifty	far fin for fir

5.	6.	7.	8.
fair fur from rut	spar spore spur spare	burn press barn purse	curb chore church curl

9.	10.	11.	12.
farm firm form fern	hard bird herd bead	rocker racket soccer rocket	pork pitcher park patches

13.	14.	15.	16.
short slant spite shirt	giraffe geranium girl gingerbread	gorge gull curl girl	barbers rubbers borders robbers

17.	18.	19.	20.
turkey turnip tricky parsnip	zebra zipper bronze sipper	forty thirteen churns thirty	seaman icebox iceman iceberg

21.	22.	23.	24.
marching morning mermaid sunset	squirt squirrel squint squeeze	spark spend speak spider	termite turtle tremble turkey

NAME _____

AR, ER, IR, OR, UR

Find the word in each box to complete the sentence. Circle the word. Then write it on the line.

1. You need to leave a margin on your _____paper_____ .	payer (paper) polar
2. The narrow street was _____ and deserted.	story hurry dirty
3. We live in a _____ city that has big skyscrapers.	furry large darts
4. A _____ is a much larger storm than a tornado.	hurricane September carpenter
5. In a city, you may _____ see birds like the thrush.	serve nerve never

Read the words that are part of each sentence. Finish the sentence by writing the words from the box in the correct order.

1. The doctor had to pull the _thorn from Bob's finger_ .	finger from Bob's thorn
2. In the fall, many _____ .	their harvest farmers crops
3. A bow and arrow _____ .	used are archery in
4. Marta received a parcel in the _____ .	mail her birthday for
5. March is the third month of the year, and _____ .	the spring of start
6. On Saturday, Dad picked parsnips _____ .	roasted and a turkey

NAME _____

Vowel Digraph Sound: OO

A vowel digraph is a double vowel that does not follow Long Vowel Rule 1.

The word **zoo** has one sound of the vowel digraph **oo**. Say the name of the picture in each box. Circle each picture with a name that has the sound of **oo**, as in **zoo**.

1.	2.	3.	4.	5.
6.	7.	8.	9.	10.
11.	12.	13.	14.	15.

Say the name of the picture in each box. Circle the name.

1. boom booth broom	2. spool spoon soon	3. hoop hoof boot	4. loose tooth booth
5. snowman snooze	6. noon moan moon	7. moose goose roost	8. load toad food
9. roaster rooster	10. tooth toothbrush	11. lagoon raccoon	12. tools stool

NAME _____

Vowel Digraph Sound: OO

Find the word in each box to complete the sentence. Circle the word. Then write it on the line.

I. The ____raccoon____ raids garbage cans.	lagoon ~~harpoon~~ (raccoon)
2. While Charles sits by the pool, he sips a _____ drink.	cool coop coat
3. Turnips and carrots are roots that we use for _____.	fool food tool
4. Did you see the rooster land outside the window of my _____?	root room road

Read the words that are part of each sentence. Finish the sentence by writing the words from the box in the correct order.

I. The baby ate his food ____with a spoon____.	a spoon with
2. Brett goes home from school for _____.	at noon lunch
3. It did not hurt when the dentist pulled _____.	tooth his loose
4. You may choose the swimming pool _____ as the place for the party.	or lagoon the
5. When the _____, you can see shadows.	full is moon
6. Our class will go to the city to _____.	zoo visit the

NAME _____

Vowel Digraph Sound: OO

The word book has the other sound of the vowel digraph oo. Say the name of the picture in each box. Circle the name. Then circle each picture with a name that has the sound of oo as in book.

1. book / boot hook / hoot	2. cookie / cake cook / nook	3. cool / cook coat / took	4. books / boats backs / boots
5. crook / crow croak / corn	6. noon / moon sows / moan	7. foot / feet fool / feel	8. book / boost hook / roost
9. girl / pole loop / pool	10. hood / hoop hook / hoof	11. wools / words woods / works	12. stood / stool flood / stoop
13. shook / school brook / shoot	14. soothe / boat loose / beat	15. spoof / spore toot / spoon	16. cookies / roost rookies / boost
17. tied / toad took / tool	18. wishbone / woodpile workbook / woodwork	19. balloon / cartoon ballroom / canteen	20. footpath / showman footman / snowman
21. dustproof / soothe toothbrush / loose	22. booster / footrest rooster / football	23. scoop / stood school / shook	24. work / woodcutter woods / woodpecker

NAME _____

Vowel Digraph Sound: OO

Find the word in each box to complete the sentence. Circle the word. Then write it on the line.

1. Morning comes before _____noon_____.	moon (noon) loon
2. Fred _____ at the window to look at the floats.	stool wood stood
3. The stones in the _____ have been worn smooth.	bark crook brook
4. We like to hike into the cool _____ and sit.	words woods wools

Read the words that are part of each sentence. Finish the sentence by writing the words from the box in the correct order.

1. A weaving loom stood in a ____corner of the room____.	room of corner the
2. When the club president greeted me, _____.	my she hand shook
3. Janice took lots of time _____.	paint to woodwork the
4. At noon, we will choose _____.	a good team football
5. Adults and children like to look at _____.	in cartoons paper the
6. Give Tommy a boost so he can _____.	reach jar cookie the

NAME _____

Vowel Digraph Sound: EA

The word <u>bread</u> has the sound of the vowel digraph <u>ea</u>. Read each word below. Write the word in the first column if the <u>ea</u> follows Long Vowel Rule 1. Write the word in the second column if the <u>ea</u> has the vowel sound you hear in <u>bread</u>.

head	treasure	beak	health	weather
seat	weapon	sweater	dream	cleanser
beads	peasant	seal	teammate	headline
feather	beaver	breakfast	eagle	teapot
thread	peach	leaf	threaten	peacock
	dread	oatmeal	peanut	

beads

NAME _____

Vowel Digraphs Sounds: AU, AW, EI

The vowel digraph <u>au</u> in <u>auto</u> and the vowel digraph <u>aw</u> in <u>hawk</u> have the same sound. Say the name of the picture in each box. Circle each picture with a name that has the sound of <u>au</u> and <u>aw</u>.

1.	2.	3.	4.	5.
6.	7.	8.	9.	10.
11.	12.	13.	14.	15.
16.	17.	18.	19.	20.
21.	22.	23.	24.	25.

The word <u>eight</u> has the sound of the vowel digraph <u>ei</u>. Read each word below. Write the word in the first column if the <u>ei</u> follows Long Vowel Rule 1. Write the word in the second column if the <u>ei</u> has the vowel sound you hear in <u>eight</u>.

eighty	reins	ceiling	seize	neither	Keith
receive	freight	veil	Sheila	weight	reindeer

_____ receive	

Vowel Digraphs

Say the name of the picture in each box. Circle the name.

1.	2.	3.	4.
(head) bead dead deal	law jaw raw paw	father leather feather lather	ate eight gate eighty
5.	6.	7.	8.
savage passage sausage message	sweeter cleanser sweater cleaner	claw squaw slaw thaw	Audrey auto August author
9.	10.	11.	12.
saucer fancy saucy faucet	eighty neighbor eight eighteen	sleigh weight weird weapons	aiming arming awning acting
13.	14.	15.	16.
deadline headstone headline leaflet	berry strawberry cranberry straw	lawyer laundry laughs launder	saucy soccer sauce saucer
17.	18.	19.	20.
breading breathless breathing breakfast	shell shawl chill crawl	freight eight eighty barge	read dread breath bread

NAME _____

Vowel Digraphs

Find the word in each box to complete the sentence. Circle the word. Then write it on the line.

1. We had a ___treasure___ hunt at Sheila's party.	weather teammate (treasure)
2. The teacher _____ us to measure paper with a ruler.	taught faucet freight
3. Art was surprised to see how sharp a tiger's _____ are.	thaws claws slaw
4. You may have to walk after a long run to catch your _____.	breath wealth health

Read the words that are part of each sentence. Finish the sentence by writing the words from the box in the correct order.

1. Give Dawn a message to ___bring home some sausage___.	some home bring sausage
2. Maud _____.	daughter is baker's the
3. When you camp, it is pleasant _____.	weather to good have
4. Bears and many other animals like _____.	raw meat eat to
5. We saw reindeer and _____.	at fawns the zoo
6. The parts of a harness used by a rider to control a _____.	the are horse reins

NAME _____

Vowel Digraphs

Play Tic-Tac-Toe. Draw a line through the three pictures in a row that have the same vowel digraph sound.

1.

2.

3.

4.

NAME _____

Diphthong Sounds: OW, OU

A <u>diphthong</u> is made up of two vowels blended together as one sound.

The diphthong <u>ow</u> in <u>cow</u> and the diphthong <u>ou</u> in <u>scout</u> have the same sound. Say the name of the picture in each box. Circle each picture with a name that has the sound of <u>ow</u> and <u>ou</u>.

Say the name of the picture in each box. Circle the name.

1.	2.	3.	4.
eel　　(owl)　 our　　vow	now　　caw cow　　bow	vowels　　towels howls　　house	scoot　　scowl score　　scout
5.	**6.**	**7.**	**8.**
crowns　　clowns crowds　　cloud	vowel　　tail tool　　towel	snout　　scout sweat　　scoot	blaze　　blouse house　　brown
9.	**10.**	**11.**	**12.**
scowl　　clean clown　　frown	shouter　　shore shower　　power	maintain　　faint mountain　　fountain	tower　　shower floor　　flower

NAME _____

Diphthong Sound: OW

Read each word below. Write the word in the first column if the <u>ow</u> follows Long Vowel Rule 1. Write the word in the second column if the <u>ow</u> has the vowel sound you hear in <u>cow</u>.

owner	drown	arrowhead	fellow	towrope
scowl	howl	power	crowd	allow
slow	towel	brown	glowworm	downtown
powder	clown	bowl	flown	rowboat
rainbow	towing	grow	mower	
snowdrift	prowler	drowsy	flower	

owner
_____

NAME _____

Diphthong Sounds: OW, OU

Find the word in each box to complete the sentence. Circle the word. Then write it on the line.

1. A dark ____cloud____ crossed the moon.	(cloud) clown proud
2. Paul found an arrowhead near a big _____ of dirt.	mount mound sound
3. Now you may measure the _____ and make the bread.	power flour flows
4. We are _____ to be good citizens of our town.	ground prowl proud

Read the words that are part of each sentence. Finish the sentence by writing the words from the box in the correct order.

1. The trip downtown ____took about an hour____.	an hour took about
2. A dog will keep prowlers _____.	from away house the
3. Will the airport allow visitors _____?	control in tower the
4. Joan saw eight cows and three _____.	the in meadow horses
5. The hot sun melts the _____ and causes spring floods.	snow the mountains on
6. We will take our own towels _____.	to pool the down

NAME _____

Diphthong Sounds: OY, OI

The diphthong oy in boy and the diphthong oi in oil have the same sound. Say the name of the picture in each box. Circle each picture with a name that has the sound of oy or oi.

1.	2.	3.	4.	5.
6.	7.	8.	9.	10.
11.	12.	13.	14.	15.

The word blew has the sound of ew. Say the name of the picture in each box. Circle each picture with a name that has the sound of ew.

1.	2.	3.	4.
5.	6.	7.	8.
9.	10.	11.	12.

NAME _____

Diphthongs

Say the name of the picture in each box. Circle the name.

1. toy / ahoy / (boy) / joy	2. drew / blew / grew / flew	3. cloud / prowl / clown / growl	4. now / own / row / cow
5. snout / snow / scowl / scout	6. owl / oil / out / oat	7. flew / screw / drew / crew	8. boys / joys / toys / ahoy
9. shower / sawed / sewer / sound	10. boil / foil / bout / pout	11. rouse / mound / mouse / found	12. towed / towel / bowed / trowel
13. soils / rains / coils / coins	14. rivalry / jewelry / joyful / jointly	15. cloud / clown / loud / crown	16. newsreel / newer / newspaper / sewer
17. blower / flower / slower / shower	18. mountain / county / fountain / bounty	19. screwdriver / chew / driven / show	20. avoiding / appoint / noisemakers / voice

NAME _____

Diphthongs

Find the word in each box to complete the sentence. Circle the word. Then write it on the line.

1. A crowd saw the _____royal_____ family board the plane.	loyal (royal) yeast
2. We must learn how to avoid _____ ivy in the woods.	person poison prison
3. Will your mother allow you to _____ the scouts?	gain pain join
4. The new ship and its _____ are days overdue.	crew screw flew

Read the words that are part of each sentence. Finish the sentence by writing the words from the box in the correct order.

1. The girls tossed the _____coins in the fountain_____.	in the fountain coins
2. If you have your choice, will you go to _____.	beach the downtown or
3. Paul was the first boy at bat because he _____.	the straw longest drew
4. The wind blew out the camper's lantern as _____.	worse storm the grew
5. The teacher will appoint a boy or girl to report on the _____.	in noise hall the
6. A crowd soon gathered on the street to enjoy the filming _____.	show a TV of

NAME _____

Diphthongs

Play Tic-Tac-Toe. Draw a line through the three pictures in a row that have the same diphthong sound.

1.

2.

3.

4.

NAME _____

Consonant Digraphs: CH, CK

Read each word below. Write the word in the first column if it has the sound ch has in cheese. Write the word in the second column if it has the sound ch and ck have in school and socks.

jacks	racket	chimney	children	teacher
echo	cheap	church	schedule	scheme
choice	nickel	chimpanzee	chocolate	character
kitchen	ranch	witch	pinch	chipmunk
chorus	cricket	picket	school	socket
chance		truck		ache

choice	

Consonant Digraphs: KN, GN, WR, PH

The digraphs <u>kn</u> and <u>gn</u> have the sound of n. The digraph <u>wr</u> has the sound of <u>r</u>. Read each work below. Underline the digraphs <u>kn</u>, <u>gn</u>, and <u>wr</u> in the words.

1. <u>kn</u>it	2. gnaw	3. wrist	4. unknown
5. write	6. knothole	7. wrench	8. typewriter
9. gnash	10. knight	11. gnat	12. wrestle
13. knee	14. unwrap	15. wrong	16. knelt
17. wring	18. knapsack	19. knife	20. wreath
21. knockout	22. wriggle	23. wreckage	24. unknot
25. writhe	26. knickknack	27. signboard	28. knowledge

The digraph <u>ph</u> has the sound of <u>f</u>. Read each word below. Write the word in the first column if it has <u>ph</u> at the beginning. Write the word in the second column if <u>ph</u> is in the middle. Write the word in the third column if <u>ph</u> is at the end.

elephant	Ralph	triumph	typhoid
telegraph	phonics	dolphin	pheasant
Phillip	photo	typhoon	nymph
telephone	phrase	paragraph	Phyllis
	digraph	diphthong	

1.	2.	3.
Phillip		
_____	_____	_____
_____	_____	_____
_____	_____	_____
_____	_____	_____
_____	_____	_____
_____	_____	_____

NAME _____

Consonant Digraphs

Say the name of the picture in each box. Circle the name.

1.	2.	3.	4.
telegraph typewriter (telephone) teletype	kneel knock knife knack	thirty third dirty tired	wrong write white writhe

5.	6.	7.	8.
pickle picked pitch nickel	wrench wreck wrap write	gnat knot gnaw spot	whale snail while wheel

9.	10.	11.	12.
known knight knife wife	wriggle wrong sting wring	chicken chipmunk kitchen chestnut	know knot knew knob

13.	14.	15.	16.
scholar school stool chorus	sign sight gnu gnarl	trick truck stuck track	elevate elephant dolphin pheasant

17.	18.	19.	20.
shop chop ship chip	pharmacy knapsack knowledge knockout	chiefs checks choice chicks	typhoid triumph typhoon typewriter

NAME _____

Consonant Digraphs

Find the word in each box to complete the sentence. Circle the word. Then write it on the line.

1. Do not forget to pack a frying pan in your _____knapsack_____.	knothole knowledge (knapsack)
2. Did you hear the echo when Phillip _____, "Hello"?	stamped shouted cheated
3. Who knows the difference between a _____ and a tornado?	typhoid typhoon typical
4. The main character in the story is a _____ chimp.	scheme changer charming
5. Each of us has heard a symphony _____ play.	orchestra elephant paragraph

Read the words that are part of each sentence. Finish the sentence by writing the words from the box in the correct order.

1. Ralph and _____Chuck like to wrestle_____.	like Chuck wrestle to
2. A large African antelope is _____.	known gnu as a
3. Phyllis sent us a _____.	herself of photo good
4. Charles found parts of a wrecked _____.	the beach on ship
5. The man passed out free tickets _____.	dolphin the show to

NAME _____

Word Ending: LE

Say the name of the picture in each box. Circle the name.

1. cattle raffle ramble (rattle)	**2.** doodle saddle handle beetle	**3.** marble candle margin maple	**4.** marble candle cactus castle
5. wishing whistle weather western	**6.** people pencil pickle tickle	**7.** handle tackle turtle startle	**8.** people pencil purple parcel
9. cycle candle circus circle	**10.** kindle knuckle hustle kettle	**11.** dangles bubbles tattles babbles	**12.** eagle ankle able apple
13. bottle bubble battle babble	**14.** thistle trestle triangle trickle	**15.** meddle nestle needle saddle	**16.** eager eagle enter large
17. tablet tangle table tingle	**18.** bundle bicycle bottle bridle	**19.** reliable resemble untangle rectangle	**20.** bottle bicycle buckle bundle

NAME _____

Word Ending: LE

Say the name of the picture in each box. Then write the missing letters.

1. t _a_ b _l_ _e_	2. c __ __ d __ __	3. __ __ __ b __ __	4. __ irc __ __
5. __ __ __ ck __ __	6. __ a __ __ __ __	7. __ __ __ e __ __ __ __	8. __ __ __ __ __ d __ __
9. __ urt __ __	10. __ h __ st __ __	11. __ __ __ ck __ e	12. __ __ __ o __ __ __ __

Find the word in each box to complete the sentence. Circle the word. Then write it on the line.

1. The shape of a bicycle wheel is a _____circle_____.	candle castle (circle)
2. The _____ was set with the fine china and silver.	tablet table tangle
3. Please pour a _____ milk into the baby's bottle, and give it to her.	little tattle letter
4. A crowd of _____ went to the lagoon in the park to see the model boat races.	bottle purple people
5. If Tom whistles for his horse, the horse will return to the _____.	settle table stable

NAME _____

Vowels Heard and Seen

Say the name of the picture in each box. On the first line write the number of vowel sounds you hear in the name. On the second line write the number of vowels you see in the name. Remember that y and w are sometimes vowels.

1.	map 1 1		13.	teapot ___ ___	
2.	eleven ___		14.	dome ___ ___	
3.	jet ___		15.	puppet ___	
4.	football ___		16.	woodpecker ___ ___	
5.	porcupine ___		17.	snowman ___ ___	
6.	head ___ ___		18.	butterfly ___ ___	
7.	sailboat ___		19.	volcano ___	
8.	eighteen ___		20.	train ___	
9.	claw ___		21.	chimney ___	
10.	kitchen ___		22.	gingerbread ___	
11.	zoo ___		23.	balloon ___ ___	
12.	sausage ___		24.	noisemakers ___	

NAME _____

84

Vowels Heard and Seen

Say the name of the picture in each box. On the first line write the number of vowel sounds you hear in the name. On the second line write the number of vowels you see in the name. Remember that y and w are sometimes vowels.

1. parrot 2 2	13. box ___ ___
2. beaver ___ ___	14. seventeen ___ ___
3. ship ___ ___	15. newspaper ___ ___
4. kangaroo ___ ___	16. chair ___ ___
5. uniform ___ ___	17. knife ___ ___
6. giraffe ___ ___	18. sled ___ ___
7. chain ___ ___	19. wheelbarrow ___ ___
8. fountain ___ ___	20. mitten ___ ___
9. propeller ___ ___	21. valentine ___ ___
10. yawn ___ ___	22. ring ___ ___
11. mermaid ___ ___	23. needle ___ ___
12. rectangle ___ ___	24. square ___ ___

NAME _____

Recognition of Syllables

You can tell the number of syllables in a word by counting the vowel sounds you hear. Say the name of the picture in each box. On the first line write the number of vowel sounds you hear in the name. On the second line write the number of vowels you see in the name. On the last line write the number of syllables in the name.

I.	hand	13.	goat
	1 1 1		___ ___ ___
2.	raccoon	14.	headline
	___ ___ ___		___ ___ ___
3.	grapes	15.	tie
	___ ___ ___		___ ___ ___
4.	beehive	16.	bicycle
	___ ___ ___		___ ___ ___
5.	cabin	17.	toys
	___ ___ ___		___ ___ ___
6.	valentine	18.	rabbit
	___ ___ ___		___ ___ ___
7.	hill	19.	window
	___ ___ ___		___ ___ ___
8.	strawberry	20.	iceberg
	___ ___ ___		___ ___ ___
9.	mule	21.	groceries
	___ ___ ___		___ ___ ___
10.	playground	22.	fence
	___ ___ ___		___ ___ ___
11.	peacock	23.	vegetables
	___ ___ ___		___ ___ ___
12.	eleven	24.	football
	___ ___ ___		___ ___ ___

NAME _____

Recognition of Syllables

You can tell the number of syllables in a word by counting the vowel sounds you hear. Say the name of the picture in each box. On the first line write the number of vowel sounds you hear in the name. On the second line write the number of vowel sounds you see in the name. On the last line write the number of syllables in the name.

#	Picture / Word		#	Picture / Word
1.	chipmunk 2 2 2		13.	tree ___ ___ ___
2.	cheese ___ ___ ___		14.	twelve ___ ___ ___
3.	sixteen ___ ___ ___		15.	fishbowl ___ ___ ___
4.	feather ___ ___ ___		16.	porcupine ___ ___ ___
5.	sheep ___ ___ ___		17.	kite ___ ___ ___
6.	grasshopper ___ ___ ___		18.	beaver ___ ___ ___
7.	screwdriver ___ ___ ___		19.	fan ___ ___ ___
8.	rooster ___ ___ ___		20.	elephant ___ ___ ___
9.	goat ___ ___ ___		21.	triangle ___ ___ ___
10.	thermometer ___ ___ ___		22.	wagon ___ ___ ___
11.	typewriter ___ ___ ___		23.	seventy-seven ___ ___ ___
12.	train ___ ___ ___		24.	volcano ___ ___ ___

NAME _____

Recognition of Syllables

To recognize a new word, you often look at and pronounce small parts, or syllables, within the word, listening to see if you can recognize them as words you have used or heard before. To do this you may need to divide a word into syllables. Here are two tips to help you divide words into syllables.

Tip 1: A one-syllable word is never divided. (pass)

Tip 2: Divide a compound word between the words that form the compound word. (bath/robe)

Divide the following words into syllables, drawing a slash between each syllable. Write the number 1 or 2 after each word to show which tip you used. Remember that you can tell the number of syllables in a word by counting the vowel sounds you hear.

pass	teapot	oatmeal	breakfast
tiptop	sandbox	plate	house
fishbowl	strand	toothbrush	flashlight
perch	tadpole	dustpan	noise
sailboat		brook	

pass _____	1	_____	____
_____	__	_____	____
_____	__	_____	____
_____	__	_____	____
_____	__	_____	____
_____	__	_____	____
_____	__	_____	____
_____	__	_____	____

NAME _____

Recognition of Syllables

Divide the following words into syllables, drawing a slash between each syllable. Write the number of 1 or 2 after each word to show which tip you used.

airport	woodpile	playpen	peanut	headline
curve	join	sagebrush	stairway	football
handcuffs	peacock	bedroom	march	beehive
iceberg	raincoat	necklace	headache	popcorn
dream	spend	proud	leaves	found
airplane		jigsaw		showmanship

____ air/port ____	2	_____	____
_____	__	_____	____
_____	__	_____	____
_____	__	_____	____
_____	__	_____	____
_____	__	_____	____
_____	__	_____	____
_____	__	_____	____
_____	__	_____	____
_____	__	_____	____
_____	__	_____	____
_____	__	_____	____
_____	__	_____	____

NAME _____

Suffixes: S, ED

Underline the base word and circle the suffix in each of the following words. Remember that a base word is a word to which a prefix or suffix may be added to form a new word.

1. bug(s)	2. failed	3. burned	4. crossed	5. rays
6. fussed	7. tamed	8. worked	9. cheered	10. thinks
11. wished	12. asked	13. fixed	14. spends	15. mailed
16. played	17. leads	18. snows	19. hatched	20. dreamed
21. puffed	22. helped	23. rained	24. plows	25. parted

Find the word in the box to complete each sentence. Circle the word. Then write the word on the line.

1. Mary will _____ lead _____ the other scouts to a secret cave.	(lead) leads
2. Will Bob be able to _____ the wrecked car?	fix fixed
3. Roger dreamed that he _____ away on a white cloud.	sail sailed
4. We have _____ our teacher to take us to the zoo.	ask asked
5. Ellen's class took their lunch and hiked up to the _____ at the top of the hill.	rock rocked
6. When the eggs were ready to _____, we saw the chicks peck their way out of the shells.	hatch hatched

NAME _____

Suffixes: ES, ED

If a base word ends in x, ss, sh, ch, or z, we usually add es, which is a syllable, to form the plural of the word. Underline the base word in the words below. Circle the suffix.

1. branch(es)	2. fuzzes	3. beads	4. wishes	5. boxes
6. taxes	7. losses	8. patches	9. sixes	10. glasses
11. ashes	12. beaches	13. kisses	14. seals	15. dishes
16. buzzes	17. axes	18. brushes	19. bosses	20. weights
21. lunches	22. passes	23. schools	24. shawls	25. thrushes
26. eggs	27. chains	28. foxes	29. witches	30. mixes
31. misses	32. cashes	33. birds	34. fizzes	35. punches

When ed is added to a base word ending in d or t, the suffix is a syllable and is pronounced ed. Circle the word that will complete the sentence. Write it on the line.

1. The boys ___coasted___ down the hill on their bicycles.	cranked / roasted / (coasted)
2. An empty raft ___ downstream with the current.	bloated / floated / planted
3. The hot sun ___ the ice before we could skate.	melted / rusted / sorted
4. Tom ___ a screw or a nail to hang up the sign.	mended / needed / rested
5. The helicopter ___ on the roof of the post office.	darted / loaded / landed
6. The girls made a windmill for a school project, and the boys ___ it.	pointed / painted / printed

NAME ___

Suffixes: S, E, ED, ING

Read the words that are part of each sentence. Finish the sentence by choosing the correct base word in the box and adding the correct suffix— s, es, ed, or ing—to it. Write the word on the line.

1. The fence along the road needs _____mending_____.	send (mend) dart
2. Scouting is good _____ for boys and girls.	track brain train
3. Roberta trimmed the bushes and the _____ of the trees with some clippers.	thrush beach branch
4. Acting out a story is more fun than _____ the story.	tell fill bell
5. Kurt places his hand over his mouth when he _____.	squint cough paint
6. Are we _____ to have fair weather for tomorrow's picnic?	go no so
7. Bill _____ because he was facing the sun, searching for his lost balloon.	spend splint squint
8. Stop! Do not run and jump into the swimming pool. It has just been _____.	dream train drain
9. The elephants are _____ the circus parade down Main Street.	lend lead deal
10. Pat enjoys _____ letters she has received since she became ill.	reach read seat
11. Did the gnu know that the lion was _____ him?	truck stand stalk

NAME _____

Suffixes: ER, EST

Underline each base word below. Circle each suffix.

1. faster fastest	2. slower slowest	3. darker darkest	4. longer longest	5. shorter shortest
6. thicker thickest	7. hardest harder	8. stiffest stiffer	9. softest softer	10. nearer nearest
11. quickest quicker	12. loudest louder	13. lower lowest	14. greenest greener	15. newest newer

Read the words that are part of each sentence. Finish the sentence by adding _er_ or _est_ to the base word in the box. Write the new word on the line.

1. Which animal is _____slower_____, a snail or a turtle?	slow
2. The _____ store is five miles down the road.	near
3. At one time, clipper ships were the _____ ships on the seas.	fast
4. To the little lambs, the grass looked _____ in the meadow across the road than in their meadow.	green
5. A rectangle is _____ than it is wide.	long
6. Our new sofa is _____ than the old one.	soft
7. My new shortcut is the _____ way to school.	quick
8. The new owners of the castle made the _____ room into the lightest room by adding windows.	dark

NAME _____

Suffixes: FUL, LESS

Underline each base word below. Circle each suffix.

1. fearful tearless	2. hopeless hopeful	3. careless careful	4. painful painless	5. fearful fearless
6. helpless helpful	7. tactful tactless	8. faithful faithless	9. useless useful	10. needless needful
11. tasteful tasteless	12. thankful thankless	13. harmful harmless	14. restless restful	15. cheerless cheerful

Read each sentence. Circle the word in the box that describes what the sentence is saying.

1. Some children cry when the barber cuts their hair.	tearful tearless
2. The mining engineers gave up the search for the lost mine.	hopeful hopeless
3. Mr. Smith saw the puppy floating on a raft in the flooded stream, and he saved it.	helpful helpless
4. We always lock all the windows and doors before we leave the house to go shopping.	careful careless
5. The children huddled in the corner of the dark, chilly room.	cheerful cheerless
6. Jill's hamburger had little flavor without salt and pepper.	tasteful tasteless
7. Kitty clung to her big sister's hand as they ran down the dark street.	fearful fearless
8. Rat and insect poisons must be kept out of children's reach.	harmful harmless

NAME _____

Suffixes: LY, NESS

Underline each base word below. Circle each suffix.

1. large**ly** largeness	2. likely likeness	3. dryness dryly	4. crossness crossly	5. closely closeness
6. shortly shortness	7. hardness hardly	8. stiffness stiffly	9. fairly fairness	10. gladness gladly
11. strangeness strangely	12. thickness thickly	13. weakly weakness	14. neatly neatness	15. quickness quickly

Read the words that are part of each sentence. Finish the sentence by adding ly or ness to the base word in the box. Write the new word on the line.

1. The ____likeness____ between Dick and his father is amazing.	like
2. Our _____ newspaper had a report about our play.	week
3. The fire chief _____ pinned badges for bravery on three members of our class.	proud
4. A diamond can scratch glass because of its _____.	hard
5. Please pass the ball _____ around the circle.	quick
6. The dog's _____ made it a nice pet for the children.	tame
7. The whiteness of the marble statue contrasts with the _____ of the velvet drape behind it.	black
8. The grocery store worker stacked the canned goods _____.	neat

NAME _____

Suffixes: EN, ABLE

Underline each base word below. Circle each suffix.

1. hard(en)	2. enjoyable	3. readable	4. blacken	5. cleanable
6. kissable	7. sicken	8. weaken	9. wearable	10. reasonable
11. strengthen	12. thicken	13. shorten	14. sweeten	15. beatable
16. trainable	17. workable	18. freshen	19. moisten	20. drinkable
21. maiden	22. sharpen	23. darken	24. quicken	25. laughable

Read the words that are part of each sentence. Finish the sentence by adding en or able to the base word in the box. Write the new word on the line.

1. Daily exercises will ___strengthen___ the muscles.	strength
2. My grandmother's shaky handwriting is not _____.	read
3. The day we spent at the carnival was most _____.	enjoy
4. This lemonade is too sour. Please _____ it for us.	sweet
5. The water at camp is so bad that it is hardly _____.	drink
6. There is so much paint on these pants that they are not _____.	wear
7. You may _____ your pencils the first thing each morning.	sharp
8. If you _____ your finger and hold it in the air, you can tell which way the wind is blowing.	moist

NAME _____

Suffixes: TION, SION

The endings tion and sion stand for sounds like shun or zhun. Read the words below. Underline each tion ending. Circle each sion ending.

1. action	2. vacation	3. division	4. motion	5. donation
6. addition	7. confusion	8. invitation	9. occasion	10. mention
11. nation	12. multiplication	13. collection	14. election	15. exception
16. pension	17. education	18. invasion	19. conclusion	20. excursion
21. notion	22. convention	23. satisfaction	24. introduction	25. subtraction

Find the word in each box to complete the sentence. Circle the word. Then write it on the line.

1. A wedding is a happy ____occasion____.	mention (occasion) aonation
2. Carla sent each classmate an _____ to her party.	convention collection invitation
3. The _____ of the subway made it hard to stand.	motion notion nation
4. Noise in a classroom causes _____ for all of us.	excursion conclusion confusion
5. Our family took an _____ boat up the river last Sunday.	excursion conclusion confusion
6. Matt invited Todd to visit during the spring _____.	addition vacation donation
7. Quick _____ saved the a boy who fell into the river.	nation action notion
8. Think about the story and write your own _____.	convention connection conclusion

NAME _____

Recognition of Syllables

Tip 1. A one-syllable word is never divided. (pass)

Tip 2. Divide a compound word between the words that form the compound word. (bath/robe)

Tip 3. When a word has a suffix, divide the word between the base word and the suffix if the suffix has a vowel sound. (fear/less)

Divide the words below into syllables, drawing a slash between each syllable. After each word write the number of the tip you used. Remember that you can tell the number of syllables in a word by counting the vowel sounds you hear.

tasteless	nation	freshen	playground
hitches	caused	quickly	neatness
cattails	telling	longest	louder
likely	faithful	pension	mended
stiff	painted	glasses	pinching

taste/less — 3

NAME

Recognition of Syllables

Divide the words below into syllables by drawing a slash between the syllables, as in the example. After each word write the number of the tip you used.

1. use/ful 3	2. haircut	3. squinting	4. planted
5. needed	6. gladly	7. helpless	8. darker
9. grapes	10. brushes	11. action	12. weakly
13. crossness	14. fearless	15. mission	16. thankful
17. greenest	18. rained	19. dryness	20. strangely
21. newer	22. sweeten	23. raincoat	24. mixes
25. dreaming	26. section	27. proudest	28. weaken
29. tasteless	30. hopeful	31. sicken	32. seacoast

Read the words that are part of each sentence. Finish the sentence by writing the words from the box in the correct order.

1. The Smiths have the _greenest lawn in town_____.	town in lawn greenest
2. It rained soon after we_____.	planting corn finished the
3. Two flash floods this past year _____.	have dam the weakened
4. Quick action by the second_____.	the saved baseman game
5. Because of its skin thickness, an elephant_____.	is easily hurt not
6. To fill the crate, we need three _____.	of boxes more berries

NAME _____

Prefixes: UN, DIS

A prefix is a syllable placed before a base word to create a new word. A prefix always has a particular meaning.

The prefixes un and dis usually reverse the meaning of a base word, as in unhappy and disobey.

Underline the base word and circle the prefix in each of the words below.

1. disclose	2. unknown	3. displease	4. discolor	5. unhandy
6. unjust	7. disown	8. dislike	9. unscrew	10. disagree
11. disable	12. unpack	13. dishonest	14. uneven	15. unused
16. unhappy	17. dislocate	18. unclaimed	19. disorder	20. discharge
21. disband	22. unwilling	23. disappear	24. untaught	25. uncertain

Find the word in each box to complete the sentence. Circle the word. Then write it on the line.

1. The post office will auction off packages that are ____unclaimed____. | unclean / uncommon / (unclaimed)

2. Paul enjoys eating string beans, but he _____ spinach. | disposes / dislikes / discolor

3. The _____ clown painted a happy expression on his face. | unloaded / unhappy / unlocked

4. The corner lot will not make a good tennis court because the ground is _____. | uneven / unfair / unearth

5. The wise prospector did not _____ the location of the new gold mine. | discard / disclose / discharge

6. You will _____ your classmates if you quit the swimming team. | disappear / displease / disagree

NAME _____

Prefixes: DE, EX

The prefix <u>de</u> usually means <u>down from</u> or <u>away from</u> or <u>the opposite of</u>, as in <u>depress</u>, <u>depart</u>, and <u>defrost</u>.

The prefix <u>ex</u> means <u>out from</u> or <u>beyond</u>, as in <u>extract</u>, <u>export</u>, and <u>exile</u>.

Circle the prefix in each of the words below.

1. (ex)change	2. depend	3. depart	4. exclaim	5. deform
6. defrost	7. exile	8. descend	9. deport	10. exhale
11. deface	12. depress	13. expand	14. explode	15. decode
16. extend	17. explain	18. define	19. defeat	20. extract
21. decrease	22. express	23. except	24. denote	25. describe
26. excuse	27. demand	28. denounce	29. demerit	30. excerpt

Find the word in each box to complete the sentence. Circle the word. Then write the word on the line.

1. When we breathe, we inhale and _____exhale_____.	excuse exile (exhale)
2. Dogs and other pets must _____ on their owners for food.	depend deport depart
3. We had to _____ the car's windshield because it was covered with ice.	describe defrost depress
4. The balloon hit a sharp object and _____.	expressed exploded exclaimed
5. Bees _____ nectar from flowers and make it into honey.	extract excuse explain
6. In the play-off game, Jan's team hopes to _____ June's team.	deform define defeat

NAME _____

Prefixes: RE, MIS

The prefix <u>re</u> usually means <u>again</u> or <u>back</u>, as in <u>refill</u> and <u>return</u>.
The prefix <u>mis</u> means <u>bad</u> or <u>wrong</u>, as in <u>mislead</u> and <u>misplace</u>.

Circle the prefix in each of the words below.

1. (mis)match	2. misfortune	3. rewire	4. misprint	5. rewrite
6. return	7. mislead	8. misplace	9. refill	10. recall
11. repeat	12. mistake	13. repave	14. misbehave	15. redo
16. reappear	17. replace	18. misgiving	19. repay	20. recopy
21. misjudge	22. renew	23. mishap	24. rejoin	25. mispronounce

Find the word in each box to complete the sentence. Circle the word. Then write it on the line.

1. Please correct the spelling ___mistake___ in the report you have written.	misdeed mismatch (mistake)
2. It is time to _____ our subscription to the newspaper.	repel renew replay
3. Be careful riding your bicycle so that you will not have a _____.	mislead misfire mishap
4. Dad can't find the car keys, so he must have _____ them.	misplaced misbehave misprint
5. The ice-cream store is closed for the winter, but it will _____ in the spring.	readjust reopen readmit
6. Betty's injured arm is better, so she will soon _____ her teammates.	misjudge rejoin repeat

NAME _____

Prefixes: A, AC, AD, IN,

The prefix <u>a</u> usually means <u>to</u>, <u>at</u>, or <u>in</u>, as in <u>asleep</u> and <u>aboard</u>.

The prefix <u>ad</u> means <u>to</u>, as in <u>adapt</u> and <u>adjoin</u>.

The prefix <u>ac</u> also means <u>to</u>, but is used before base words beginning with <u>c</u>, <u>k</u>, or <u>q</u>, as in <u>accustom</u>, <u>acknowledge</u>, and <u>acquit</u>.

The prefix <u>in</u> means <u>in</u> or <u>not</u>, as in <u>instep</u> and <u>incurable</u>.

Circle the prefix in each of the words below.

1. asleep	2. inflate	3. accept	4. aboard	5. inside
6. invent	7. adrift	8. admit	9. acclaim	10. alike
11. accuse	12. inhuman	13. apart	14. away	15. address
16. awhile	17. amass	18. invite	19. acquire	20. across
21. involve	22. account	23. agree	24. include	25. ablaze
26. avert	27. incurable	28. adjust	29. alight	30. indigestion

Find the word in each box to complete the sentence. Circle the word. Then write it on the line.

1. His little sister asked him to ____address____ the birthday card.	(address) adjoin adjust
2. Because of injuries, several of the team's players are _____.	instep inactive inflame
3. When a train is ready to leave a station, the conductor shouts, "All _____."	agree awhile aboard
4. Will you include me in the list of people you _____ to your party?	invite invent involve
5. If you _____ the invitation, you must help to make the party a success.	access accept accent

NAME _____

Recognition of Syllables

Tip 1: A one-syllable word is never divided. (pass)

Tip 2: Divide a compound word between the words that form the compound word. (bathrobe)

Tip 3: When a word has a suffix, divide the word between the base word and the suffix if the suffix has a vowel sound. (fear/less)

Tip 4: When a word has a prefix, divide the word between the prefix and the base word. (un/fair)

Divide the words below into syllables, drawing a slash between each syllable. After each word, write the number of the tip you used. You may need to use more than one tip to divide some words.

invite	airplane	extending	rained
accepted	involve	admit	depress
dream	defroster	discharge	acquit
misplace	disclose	unfairly	unscrew
expanded	displaying	resharpen	misbehave

in/vite	4		

NAME _____

Recognition of Syllables

Divide the words below into syllables by drawing a slash between the syllables, as in the example. Some words may have one syllable.

1. aboard	2. accept	3. except	4. abide
5. unlikely	6. define	7. discuss	8. express
9. streets	10. admit	11. forecasting	12. wakeful
13. inquire	14. undress	15. burned	16. unreal
17. disgrace	18. decidedly	19. awhile	20. mistake
21. kindness	22. handsprings	23. rephrase	24. exported
25. remoisten	26. defenseless	27. distrustful	28. misprinting
29. repeatedly	30. unshaven	31. seaside	32. disjointed

Read the words that are part of each sentence. Finish the sentence by writing the words from the box in the correct order.

1. Please accept this gift as an _____ expression of my thanks _____.	of my expression thanks
2. After school there will be a contest to _____.	gymnastics decide the champion
3. Think beforehand what you will need to _____.	take trip your on
4. Perhaps I can answer your question _____.	it you if rephrase
5. Mom has repeatedly told us to take off our muddy _____.	the door at shoes
6. All of the Jones family are going to the beach except the father, _____.	has work to who

NAME _____

Recognition of Syllables

Tip 5: When two or more consonants come between two vowels, the word is usually divided between the first two consonants. (bet/ter) Do not split blends or digraphs.

Divide the words below into syllables by drawing a slash between the syllables.

1. com/plete	2. pencil	3. confess	4. sudden
5. torment	6. necklace	7. practice	8. target
9. purple	10. children	11. surprise	12. contents
13. shallow	14. dictate	15. picture	16. pretzel
17. handy	18. rubbers	19. kitchen	20. postman

Read the words that are part of each sentence. Finish the sentence by writing the words from the box in the correct order.

1. The police perform an important _____ service for our community _____.	service our for community
2. Christine and Colleen like to _____.	basketball after play school
3. Jan's pretty purple balloon got caught in the _____.	tree branches a of
4. Children like to wade _____.	in shallow the water
5. Theresa went to the kitchen _____.	ate some and pretzels
6. The visit from the prince was a _____.	to princess the surprise

NAME _____

Recognition of Syllables

Tip 1: A one-syllable word is never divided. (pass)

Tip 2: Divide a compound word between the words that form the compound word. (bathrobe)

Tip 3: When a word has a suffix, divide the word between the base word and the suffix if the suffix has a vowel sound. (fear/less)

Tip 4: When a word has a prefix, divide the word between the prefix and the base word. (un/fair)

Tip 5: When two or more consonants come between two vowels in a word, the word is usually divided between the first two consonants. (bet/ter) Do not split blends or digraphs.

Divide the words below into syllables, drawing a slash between each syllable. After each word write the number or numbers of the tips you used.

knife	surfboard	foxes	matchbox
restless	blackness	slower	depart
discarded	quickly	nearest	wrench
downspout	respectfully	extension	reception

knife	1		

NAME _____

Divide the words below into syllables by drawing a slash between the syllables, as in the example. Some words may have one syllable.

1. nar/row/est	2. sunset	3. ungrateful	4. goblin
5. serpents	6. longer	7. mountain	8. uncommon
9. please	10. adoption	11. accepted	12. misgiving
13. census	14. hollowness	15. underline	16. chapter
17. remember	18. readjusted	19. picnicking	20. circus
21. perfectly	22. combine	23. turnpike	24. better
25. describe	26. best	27. disappear	28. cellophane
29. sandwiches	30. misspell	31. consistently	32. uncertain

Read the words that are part of each sentence. Finish the sentence by writing the words from the box in the correct order.

1. Faster driving is permitted on turnpikes but __not on city streets__ .	not city on streets
2. Please ask questions if you do not _____ .	lesson understand the perfectly
3. Picnicking has been banned in the state park _____ .	dry the weather during
4. One person in the class will describe an object, and guessing the object will _____ .	a game good make
5. Rose is a better all-around athlete than Ellen, but Ellen _____ .	better is swimming at
6. David said, "I think the best act in the circus _____ .	act is trapeze the
7. The entrance to the cave was _____ .	be to narrow found

NAME _____

Recognition of Syllables

Tip 6: When a single consonant comes between two vowels in a word, the word is usually divided after the consonant if the first vowel has a short sound. (cam/el)

Tip 7: When a single consonant comes between two vowels in a word, the word is usually divided before the consonant if the first vowel has a long sound. (tu/lip)

Say the name of the picture in each box. Then look at the word. Notice whether the first vowel has a long or short sound when a single consonant comes between two vowels. Use any tips that you know to divide the words into syllables. Write the syllables on the lines.

1.	wagon — wag on	2.	meter		
3.	tiger	4.	peanut		
5.	beaver	6.	cabin		
7.	seven	8.	spider		
9.	tomato	10.	robot		
11.	lemon	12.	volcano		
13.	blossom	14.	giraffe		
15.	dragon	16.	shadow		
17.	newspaper	18.	propeller		
19.	valentine	20.	groceries		

NAME _____

Recognition of Syllables

Divide the following words into syllables, drawing a slash between each syllable. Write the number 6 or 7 after each word to show which tip you used.

duty	robot	lilac	tulip
river	camel	metal	pedal
melon	meter	zero	second
timid	polite	begin	label
never	secret	minus	pecan
habit	punish	damage	stupid
travel	denim	magic	nature

du/ty	7		

NAME _____

Recognition of Syllables

Divide the words below into syllables by drawing a slash between the syllables, as in the example. Some words have one syllable.

1. price/less	2. bookshelf	3. clever	4. train
5. moment	6. fairest	7. defroster	8. confusion
9. nighttime	10. chance	11. cheerful	12. pilot
13. refund	14. visit	15. detergent	16. unjustly
17. cellophane	18. notice	19. robin	20. misprint
21. occasion	22. accustom	23. stairway	24. Helen
25. promise	26. surprisingly	27. introduction	29. expressive
29. dinosaur	30. dislocation	31. sweetness	32. fairgrounds

Find the word in each box to complete the sentence. Circle the word. Then write it on the line.

1. Seventy _____minus_____ fifty equals twenty. — clever / (minus) / melon

2. Philip wants to _____ around the world. — triangle / turtle / travel

3. The appearance of the robins seemed like the _____ of an early spring. — perfect / priceless / promise

4. Please follow _____ the instructions for making the paper birds. — carefully / unjustly / strangely

5. The pencil sharpener has _____ holes for different-sized pencils and crayons. — polite / second / several

6. Jim raced his _____ and won the race by a mile. — beaver / bicycle / bandit

7. Dad takes several sandwiches, fruit, and cookies in his lunch _____. — locket / bucket / booklet

NAME _____

Recognition of Syllables

> **Tip 8:** When a vowel is sounded alone in a word, it forms a syllable in itself. (e/ven)

Divide the words below into syllables, drawing a slash between each syllable.

unequal	gelatin	monument	telegraph
alarm	elephant	chemical	uniform
animals	telephone	adore	comedy
eleven	monitor	catalog	capital
benefit	ahead	cabinet	alibi
magazine	celebrate	delegate	depositor

un/e/qual
_____

_____   _____

_____   _____

_____   _____

_____   _____

_____   _____

_____   _____

_____   _____

_____   _____

_____   _____

NAME _____

Recognition of Syllables

Tip 9: When two vowels come together in a word and are sounded separately, divide the word between the two vowels. (po/em)

Divide the words below into syllables, drawing a slash between each syllable.

diet	pliers	radio	violin
lion	cameo	graduate	polio
violets	diagram	ideal	giant
piano	rodeo	casual	burial
realize	theater	create	annual
anxiety	science	diamond	continual

di/et

NAME _____

Recognition of Syllables

Say the name of each picture. Use any tips and rules that you know to help divide the words into syllables. Write the syllables on the lines.

1. ___ ___	2. ___ ___
3. ___ ___	4. ___ ___
5. ___ ___ ___	6. ___ ___
7. ___ ___ ___	8. ___ ___
9. ___ ___	10. ___ ___
11. ___ ___ ___	12. ___ ___ ___

Find the word that will complete each sentence. Circle the word. Then write the word on the line.

1. Jim and I saw a good ___comedy___ show at the local theater last week.	casual (comedy) catalog
2. Children's _____ usually contain games and puzzles as well as stories.	monuments mountains magazines
3. The boys and girls displayed their well-trained pets in the _____ parade.	animal anxiety alphabet
4. Helen soon _____ that the trail was steeper than she had thought.	radiator refilled realized
5. The eleven men on each of the competing football teams were about _____ in size and weight.	elevator equal evenly

NAME _____

Recognition of Syllables

Tip 10: When a word ends in <u>ckle</u>, divide the word between the <u>k</u> and the <u>le</u>. When a word ending in <u>le</u> is preceded by any other consonant, divide the word before that consonant. (pick/le, bub/ble)

Divide the words below into syllables, drawing a slash between each syllable.

ramble	cradle	bridle	reliable	eagle	enjoyable	tattle
able	riddle	speckle	bicycle	fable	ankle	puzzle
tangle	buckle	rumble	simple	scribble	raffle	trickle
settle	purple	sprinkle	battle	resemble	saddle	tackle

ram/ble
_____

_____   _____

_____   _____

_____   _____

_____   _____

_____   _____

_____   _____

_____   _____

_____   _____

_____   _____

_____   _____

NAME _____

Recognition of Syllables

Say the name of each picture. Write its name on the line, drawing a slash between syllables.

1. _____ta/ble_____	2. _____	3. _____	4. _____
5. _____	6. _____	7. _____	8. _____
9. _____	10. _____	11. _____	12. _____

Find the word that will complete the sentence. Circle the word. Then write the word on the line.

1. Don _____settled_____ an argument between Jean and Clare.	saddled sampled (settled)
2. A _____ holds a belt together.	bucket bicycle buckle
3. Ralph enjoyed telling _____ and Myrtle preferred to solve them.	riddles rambles rumbles
4. The baby girl _____ her sister.	reliable scribbles resembles
5. The _____ were petrified because the rattlesnake was coiled and ready to strike.	puzzle purple people

NAME _____

Recognition of Syllables

**Read each tip. Use the tip to divide the words below it into syllables.
Draw a slash between each syllable.**

Tip 1: A one-syllable word is never divided.

pass   thick   grapes   plant

Tip 2: Divide a compound word between the words that form the compound word.

football   flagpole   earthquake   stairway

Tip 3: When a word has a suffix, divide the word between the base word and the suffix if the suffix has a vowel sound.

painted   wishing   fearless   neatness

Tip 4: When a word has a prefix, divide the word between the prefix and the base word.

dispute   unfair   defrost   explain

Tip 5: When two or more consonants come between two vowels in a word, the word is usually divided between the first two consonants. Do not split blends or digraphs.

princess   balloon   surprise   pretzel

Tip 6: When a single consonant comes between two vowels in a word, the word is usually divided after the consonant if the first vowel has a short sound.

wagon   camel   shadow   seven

Tip 7: When a single consonant comes between two vowels in a word, the word is usually divided before the consonant if the first vowel has a long sound.

tulip   beaver   locate   spider

Tip 8: When a vowel is sounded alone in a word, it forms a syllable in itself.

even   uniform   alarm   cabinet

Tip 9: When two vowels come together in a word and are sounded separately, divide the word between the vowels.

poem   rodeo   create   piano

Tip 10: When a word ends in ckle, divide the word between the k and the le. When a word ending in le is preceded by any other consonant, divide the word before that consonant.

pickle   eagle   buckle   startle

NAME _____

Recognition of Syllables

Divide the words below into syllables by drawing a slash between the syllables, as in the example. Some words have one syllable.

1. glass/es	2. dreaming	3. thicken	4. quickly
5. louder	6. neatness	7. conclusion	8. pointed
9. orchestra	10. enjoyable	11. landed	12. boxes
13. census	14. lunches	15. chimpanzee	16. triumph
17. thankful	18. proudly	19. disrespectful	20. departing
21. trucked	22. connection	23. birds	24. shortest
25. airplane	26. extension	27. paragraph	28. hyphen
29. screwdriver	30. weaken	31. squinting	32. brushes
33. weights	34. moisten	35. tasteless	36. likeness
37. agreeable	38. unpunished	39. strengthen	40. examination
41. excursion	42. misconception	43. president	44. muskmelon
45. departed	46. rattlesnake	47. disappear	48. helicopter

Read the words that are part of each sentence. Finish the sentence by writing the words from the box in the correct order.

1. Bob has a pet chimpanzee _____.	mimics exactly that him
2. Janet's chances of dicovering _____.	very gold remote are
3. We flew in a helicopter _____.	low a at altitude
4. When you divide words into syllables, use _____.	syllables between hyphens the
5. Ray delivered a load of packages to _____.	office yesterday post the

NAME _____

Adding Suffixes

When a word that ends in **y** is preceded by a consonant, change the **y** to **i** before adding a suffix other than **ing**.

Add the suffixes es and ed to each base word below.

cry	1. cries	2. cried
spy	3.	4.
dry	5.	6.
try	7.	8.
deny	9.	10.
copy	11.	12.
hurry	13.	14.

When a word ends with a silent **e**, we usually drop the **e** from the base word before adding **ed** or **ing**.

Add the suffixes ed and ing to each base word below.

use	1. used	2. using
bake	3.	4.
like	5.	6.
vote	7.	8.
save	9.	10.
share	11.	12.
wipe	13.	14.

NAME _____

Adding Suffixes

> When a short vowel word ends in a single consonant, we usually double the consonant before adding the suffix.

Add the suffixes ed and ing to each base word below.

can	1. canned	2. canning
dim	3.	4.
sun	5.	6.
beg	7.	8.
kiss	9.	10.
trim	11.	12.
clap	13.	14.

Using the three tips for adding suffixes, add er and est to each base word below.

safe	1. safer	2. safest
sad	3.	4.
thin	5.	6.
funny	7.	8.
brave	9.	10.
long	11.	12.
happy	13.	14.
slow	15.	16.

NAME _____

Adding Suffixes

Read the words that are part of each sentence. Finish the sentence by adding a suffix to the base word in the box. Write the new word on the line.

1. On a long hike, the last mile is the ____hardest____.	hard
2. Shopping is lots of fun for some people, but _____ for others.	bore
3. Jill and her classmates _____ the classroom for the meeting last night.	decorate
4. Ronald _____ a tune while he was riding his bicycle.	hum
5. It is a good idea to get used to _____ with others.	share
6. There is no use _____ that you will feel bad if you do not get a part in the class play.	deny
7. The old road into town is _____ than the new highway.	short
8. Today is the _____ day so far this year.	hot
9. Theresa was the _____ girl at camp. She saved one of the other campers from drowning.	brave
10. It is too warm outside to wear that shirt, so wear a _____ one.	thin
11. The children roared when the clown performed his _____ trick.	funny

NAME _____

Contractions

Draw a line joining two words in the first column of each box to their contraction in the second column.

have not	didn't	they will	I'll	we are	it's
is not	hasn't	you will	we'll	it is	she's
did not	aren't	he will	he'll	he is	you're
has not	don't	she will	they'll	you are	we're
are not	haven't	I will	she'll	they are	he's
do not	isn't	we will	you'll	she is	they're

you have	let's	does not	can't	there is	what's
they have	we've	was not	wouldn't	that is	there'll
I have	I'm	can not	doesn't	what is	there's
we have	I've	will not	couldn't	where is	it'll
I am	they've	would not	wasn't	there will	that's
let us	you've	could not	won't	it will	where's

Read each sentence and form the contraction for each underlined group of words. Write the contraction on the line in the box.

1. I want Phil to meet Janice and Cathy. <u>They are</u> my best friends.	___ They're ___
2. We are happy that Jack <u>did not</u> wreck the model cars.	_____
3. Look! There goes Mary Smith. <u>She is</u> the winner of the safety slogan contest.	_____
4. If you <u>do not</u> like our plans for the picnic, you can make new ones.	_____
5. Sam and Trudy are going to Tommy's house when <u>they have</u> finished their homework.	_____

NAME _____

Contractions

Write the two words from which each contraction below is made.

1. he'll _____

2. wasn't _____

3. aren't _____

4. don't _____

5. they've _____

6. where's _____

7. let's _____

8. there'll _____

9. I'm _____

10. can't _____

11. she's _____

12. that's _____

13. we're _____

14. weren't _____

15. it's _____

16. couldn't _____

17. you'll _____

18. won't _____

Read the words that are part of each sentence. Circle the words in the box that will finish the sentence. Then write the contraction for those words on the line.

1. Richard tried but _____ win the transistor radio at the school carnival.	are not it is did not
2. _____ it thoughtful of the boys and girls to send Mark letters when he was in the hospital?	Will not Was not Does not
3. Ellen, _____ hurry and change clothes so we can be first in the pool.	we are we have let us
4. I am going to a party at Judy's house. _____ her birthday.	It is I am I have
5. Here's a drawing _____ very well done.	that is there will here is

NAME _____

Synonyms

Draw a line joining the words in each box that have the same meaning or almost the same meaning.

moist	hurt	bashful	finish	join	middle
injure	tell	fearful	follow	mailman	connect
choose	small	complete	shy	quiet	neat
relate	select	level	even	center	postman
little	damp	trail	afraid	tidy	still
stay	remain	glass	glisten	dispute	lie
ablaze	happiness	sharp	show	deface	ask
starch	rapidly	sparkle	keen	inquire	argument
gladness	stiffen	useful	tumbler	untruth	mar
quickly	aflame	display	helpful	expand	enlarge
repeat	within	brave	simple	allow	closest
mistake	bearded	blend	fearless	unfasten	unusual
inside	avenue	far	whole	nearest	loosen
street	error	easy	distant	uncommon	animal
unshaven	retell	total	mix	beast	permit

Finish each sentence by adding a synonym for the word in the box. Write the synonym on the line.

1. Patty's birthday package was too _____large_____ for her to carry.	big
2. Fran has the bad habit of being _____ for school.	late
3. If these bananas are not eaten at once, they will _____.	rot
4. The _____ bird sat on the windowsill.	small
5. I am _____ that all of you enjoyed Tim's party.	glad

NAME _____

Antonyms

Draw a line joining the words that have the opposite meaning.

pretty	noisy	full	cold	hard	dirty
dull	slow	warm	cool	asleep	soft
quiet	ugly	hot	well	strong	fearless
useful	bright	sick	empty	clean	weak
fast	useless	smile	frown	fearful	awake
inside	return	level	stop	first	last
tall	lower	painless	short	fall	helpful
raise	short	long	forbid	helpless	unspoken
climb	descend	allow	uneven	spoken	small
leave	outside	start	painful	large	rise
purchase	sadness	sweet	like	join	disagree
gladness	sell	wise	export	cause	deflate
longest	untidy	hate	lie	agree	separate
neat	inaction	truth	sour	far	prevent
action	shortest	import	foolish	inflate	near

Finish each sentence by adding an antonym for the word in the box.
Write the antonym on the line.

1. Joan, it is time to turn the light ____off____ and go to sleep.	on
2. Bill, you will find your socks _____ your chair.	over
3. These bakery rolls taste good because they are nice and _____.	stale
4. Carlos, do you dream a lot when you are _____?	awake
5. Jenny spread a _____ layer of peanut butter on her bread.	thin

NAME _____

Read the pair of words in each box. Write an A if the words are antonyms. Write an S if the words are synonyms.

1. pretty / ugly ___A___	**2.** moist / damp _____	**3.** empty / full _____
4. trail / follow _____	**5.** enlarge / expand _____	**6.** truth / falsehood _____
7. cause / prevent _____	**8.** longest / shortest _____	**9.** stay / remain _____
10. allow / forbid _____	**11.** complete / finish _____	**12.** wise / foolish _____
13. unusual / uncommon _____	**14.** join / separate _____	**15.** unshaven / bearded _____

Read the words that are part of each sentence. Finish the sentence by writing the words from the box in the correct order.

1. Bill's room is always neat, while his sister's ___room is always untidy___.	is / room / always / untidy
2. The balloon deflated overnight, so we will _____.	to / it / reinflate / have
3. Our cat Tab, climbed a tall oak tree, but it was _____.	afraid / it / descend / to
4. Dad is going to sell his old car and _____.	one / new / purchase / a
5. It is usually so noisy here that _____.	strange / quietness / the / seems

NAME _____

Homonyms

Draw a line joining the words in each box that sound alike.

chord	not	son	heal	made	right
too	hear	road	sun	sew	sow
knot	cent	weak	rap	write	maid
sent	cord	heel	rode	beet	sail
here	two	wrap	week	sale	beat

sea	tail	pane	due	tee	steal
tale	dye	fair	buy	prince	ring
blue	pale	by	pain	steel	nose
die	blew	dew	read	knows	tea
pail	see	reed	fare	wring	prints

daze	bow	peek	site	weight	gait
led	ate	bear	peak	gate	night
eight	lead	sight	our	reign	I
bough	days	one	bare	knight	rain
steak	stake	hour	won	eye	wait

Finish each sentence by adding homonyms for the words in the box. Write the homonyms on the lines.

1. On the _____way_____ to Deer Forest, a _____bee_____ stung Tom on his arm.	weight be
2. The ball game will begin in just _____ _____.	won our
3. Betty _____ _____ books during our spring vacation.	red too
4. Donna got a _____ fishing _____ for her birthday.	knew real
5. The first time Don _____ the ball, he _____ a basket.	through maid

NAME _____

Synonyms, Antonyms, Homonyms

**Read the pair of words in each box. Write an S if the words are synonyms.
Write an A if the words are antonyms. Write an H if the words are homonyms.**

1. bear bare H	2. separate part _____	3. smile frown _____
4. falsehood untruth _____	5. knows nose _____	6. asleep awake _____
7. gladness sadness _____	8. incomplete unfinished _____	9. days daze _____
10. large huge _____	11. sight site _____	12. unwise foolish _____
13. rain reign _____	14. ascend descend _____	15. rapidly quickly _____

**Read the words that are part of each sentence. Finish the sentence by
writing the words from the box in the correct order.**

1. A beautiful sight waited for us at the ___site of the camp___ .	camp the of site
2. John ran rapidly, but Dave _____ .	just as ran quickly
3. Sue was asleep at seven so she _____ .	be would early awake
4. This large dog _____ .	paws really has huge
5. Mary says her nose always _____ .	for what's dinner knows

NAME _____

Crossword Puzzle Review

Work the crossword puzzle.

Across

1. one section of a house
4. homonym of <u>cent</u>
7. synonym of <u>inside</u>
8. people go to a restaurant to _____
10. rhymes with <u>door</u>
11. homonym of <u>mails</u>
13. antonym of <u>open</u>
15. very clean
17. antonym of <u>stop</u>
18. a small bit of water from a faucet
20. lose some color
21. red, blue or yellow
22. homonym of <u>pair</u>
23. antonym of <u>hard</u>

Down

1. edges of cups
2. on top of
3. homonym of <u>meet</u>
4. one part of stairs
5. homonym of <u>know</u>
6. antonym of <u>false</u>
9. boy's nickname
11. what an orchestra plays
12. something sweet
16. a small pole
18. antonym of <u>shallow</u>
19. antonym of <u>rich</u>
20. homonym of <u>four</u>

NAME _____